Complementary Medicine

ISSUES

(formerly Issues for the Nineties)

Volume 53

Editor

Craig Donnellan

Independence

Educational Publishers

Cambridge

First published by Independence
PO Box 295
Cambridge CB1 3XP
England

British Library Cataloguing in Publication Data
Complementary Medicine – (Issues Series)
I. Donnellan, Craig II. Series
615.5

ISBN 1 86168 156 9

Printed in Great Britain
The Burlington Press
Cambridge

Typeset by
Claire Boyd

Cover
The illustration on the front cover is by
Pumpkin House.

CONTENTS

Introduction

Complementary Medicine is the fifty-third volume in the **Issues** series. The aim of this series is to offer up-to-date information about important issues in our world.

Complementary Medicine looks at the different kinds of complementary therapies and the debate behind the subject.

The information comes from a wide variety of sources and includes:
Government reports and statistics
Newspaper reports and features
Magazine articles and surveys
Literature from lobby groups
and charitable organisations.

It is hoped that, as you read about the many aspects of the issues explored in this book, you will critically evaluate the information presented. It is important that you decide whether you are being presented with facts or opinions. Does the writer give a biased or an unbiased report? If an opinion is being expressed, do you agree with the writer?

Complementary Medicine offers a useful starting-point for those who need convenient access to information about the many issues involved. However, it is only a starting-point. At the back of the book is a list of organisations which you may want to contact for further information.

*****

What is complementary medicine?

Information from the Institute for Complementary Medicine

Complementary Medicine (CM) includes many different techniques of treating a patient. These are based on systems practised thousands of years ago and can in fact be considered to be the original forms of medicine. They all have one aspect in common which is that they treat the patient as a whole person rather than treating a specific symptom or symptoms. They do this by treating the life force of the patient at their physical, mental and emotional levels.

Some people used to refer to CM as 'Fringe' or 'Alternative' because they consider it to be alternative to the 'Allopathic Medicine' that is practised by the General Medical Practitioners (GP's). But CM complements the needs of the patient and is a more accurate description as this term describes the methods of healing that treat the complete or whole person. Hence 'Complementary Medicine' is the most appropriate title.

Below are some of the main disciplines of Complementary Medicine.

Aromatherapy:
Science of Essential Oils.

Chinese Medicine:
Acupuncture, Acupressure, Chinese Herbs, Feng Shui, Tai Chi, Chinese Arts and Exercise, Chi Gong and Modern Acupuncture.

Colour Therapy:
Chromotology and Colour Healing.

Counselling:
– in many forms and Counselling Skills.

Energy Medicine:
Bio-Resonance, Bio-energy, Cellatronics, Rebirthing, Polarity Therapy, Electro-Crystal Therapy, Earth Breathing, Medical Dowsing, Geo-Rheology and Radionics.

Healing:
Spiritual, Dynamic, Religious, Crystal, Therapeutic Touch, Metaphysical Counselling, Reiki, Johrey and others.

Homoeopathy:
Classical, Complex and Revolutionised.

Hypnotherapy and Psychotherapy:
Psychotherapeutic Hypnosis, Structured Hypnosis, Neuro Linguistic Programming, Psycho-Systems Analysis and other techniques.

Indian Medicine:
Yoga, Ayurveda and Head Massage.

Japanese Medicine and Vietnamese Medicine:
Amatsu, Shiatsu, Katsu and others.

Naturopathy and Nutrition:
Nutrition Counselling, Dietary Therapy and Vitamin Therapy.

Physical Medicine:
Chiropractic Techniques, Osteopathic Techniques, Remedial Massage, Cranial Resonance, Bowen Technique, Pilates, Rolfing, Hellerwork, Feldenkrais, Active Balance, Alexander Technique and Bates Eye Care.

Reflexology:
Morrell Reflexology, Gentle Touch Reflexology, Advanced Reflexology, Ingham Method and others.

Massage:
Swedish, Sport, Holistic, Tuina, On-Site, Japanese, Thai, Indian and others.

Phytotherapy:
Herbalism (Western and Chinese) and Bach Flower Remedies.

Stress Control:
Biofeedback, Relaxation, Meditation, Music, Dance and Movement.

Diagnostic Techniques and Treatment:
Iridology, Kinesiology and others.

Health Sciences:
Administration and Personal Development at the appropriate levels.

© 2000 ICM (*Institute for Complementary Medicine*)

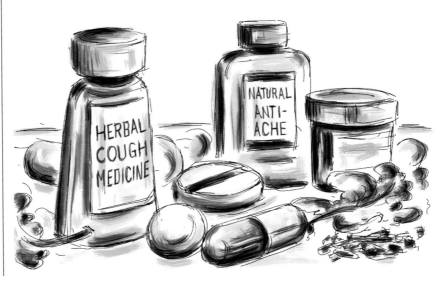

Herbal cocktails to lead revolution in medicines

By Charles Arthur,
Technology Editor

Herbal remedies will lead a revolution in medical treatment within 10 years, using ancient recipes with thousands of active compounds instead of pharmaceuticals with a single active element, scientists predict.

Dr John Wilkinson, of the University of Middlesex, said that he will tell the British Association meeting tomorrow that herbs such as sage contain groups of chemicals which interact, and have more effect combined than separately.

Meanwhile, a company called Oxford Natural Products will this year start the first-ever clinical trials of a herbal extract to treat painful periods and hip pains in women. The product is based on three traditional Chinese medicines, and results of the work should be available in about 18 months.

Dr Wilkinson said that such trials, and his own work on the common herb sage – which in extract form may be used to treat Alzheimer's Disease – suggest that the medical profession is moving towards an entirely new stage in the development of treatments.

'We are going to see a second generation of herbal medicines which will be truly pharmaceutical versions of the original product. They will still be available over the counter in health food shops, but also prescribed by GPs.' Key to the new development is an acceptance by the scientific and medical professions of the complexity and subtlety of ancient natural treatments for a range of illnesses, he said. 'We could see the first effects in two or three years, though I think realistically this is 10 to 20 years from common use.'

Herbal medicines have recently made rapid strides: earlier this month St John's wort was shown to treat depression with fewer side-effects than pharmaceuticals. Other products that show promise are monks' pepper – a herb used in monasteries in the Middle Ages to depress libido – yam extract and cannabis, which many multiple sclerosis sufferers use to relieve their symptoms.

'Pharmaceutical companies tend to focus on one active compound, but we are taking a holistic view, looking at extracts which contain thousands of different molecules,' he said. 'We accept that often the herbal extract – produced by boiling or whatever – works as a treatment, but if you try to use a single compound it doesn't. So we're trying to understand the synergy between those molecules. It's like listening to music – you can listen to one note, or to chords. With one note all the time it becomes boring. Medicine is moving on to chords.'

Sage contains chemicals which slow the action of an enzyme called acetylcholinesterase (Ace): slowing down Ace activity in the brain is important to improve the development of memories. 'We have looked at individual compounds in the extract, but the extract is more active than any single compound in it,' said Dr Wilkinson. 'We have to use artificial intelligence systems to point out which are the best combinations of compounds to include: sometimes we find that some chemicals in the extract actually reduce its potency.'

Dr Peter Hoyland, chief executive of Oxford Natural Products, said: 'The synergy effect with these extracts is real. And there is also the advantage that these extracts are often less toxic than a new synthesised chemical.'

The study into a herbal treatment for period pains will recruit 80 volunteers by the end of the year. 'About two-thirds of women in the UK have painful periods, and three-quarters of them report that it is debilitating,' said Dr Stephen Kennedy, a reader in gynaecology at the University of Oxford. 'Two-thirds of those with pain take something for it. But nobody knows how effective those medicines actually are.'

Complementary therapies

A patient-led revolution

After more than 60 years concentrating on laboratory-based science, the Arthritis Research Campaign is launching a major new initiative to fund research into complementary therapies. *Arthritis Today* looks at the background.

Over the past few years there has been an explosion of interest in complementary therapies among the general public. The media is equally obsessed – open any broadsheet or tabloid and you'll find pages of articles and advertisements enthusiastically proclaiming the virtues of Devil's Claw, St John's Wort and glucosamine sulphate.

Despite the public enthusiasm for non-conventional remedies, the medical profession – including most of the rheumatological community – continues to regard any substance or technique that has not undergone scrupulous clinical trials and/or extensive research with the utmost scepticism, not to say downright hostility.

But the fact remains that many people with arthritis are deeply dissatisfied with traditional, drug-based therapies offered to them by medics. They don't want to simply stuff themselves with pills which can have drastic side-effects or may not work anyway. Patients want to feel as though they are doing something for themselves, taking control, being listened to – and taken seriously.

Much complementary therapy, including homeopathy, herbalism, hypnotherapy and acupuncture, remains scientifically unproven. But that doesn't stop one in three people in the UK having tried it – twice that number among people with chronic conditions. Sixty-six per cent of rheumatoid arthritis patients use complementary therapy. They can't all be wrong or misguided. And although the power of the placebo is strong – often around 30 per cent – if something makes you feel better what's wrong with taking it?

The problem is, that among the many entirely competent, qualified and effective practitioners of complementary therapies, there are many who are not. And there are many therapies that veer into the lunatic fringe. It's hard for the public to know which ones to take seriously. Magnet therapy? Copper bangles? Coral calcium? MSM? Many people end up paying a lot of money for unproven products.

For these reasons there is a real need for scientific evidence to prove or disprove the effectiveness of complementary therapies. And until very recently, there has never been the will by organisations with sufficient clout or financial backup to do anything about it.

Now the ARC has decided to direct some of its resources into investigating various forms of complementary therapy. In fact, it has already started – in February it awarded its first-ever project grant to a Newcastle doctor to carry out a clinical trial into the effects of acupuncture in patients with osteo-arthritis of the knee.

Patients want to feel as though they are doing something for themselves, taking control, being listened to – and taken seriously

---

Chief executive of the ARC, Fergus Logan, explains: 'New medicines and treatments have traditionally been developed under a convention which says in a nutshell: "Don't use it if you can't prove it." But in complementary medicine, it is often believed that the proof is provided by use – and that no further investigation is needed. Scientists find this concept difficult – hence the scepticism some feel.

'We are hoping to bridge the gap by devising ways of researching complementary therapies which will provide the rigour science requires without scaring off the complementary therapists.

'The first step is to put the two in touch with each other, so that traditional scientists can explain to prospective complementary researchers the sort of questions they need to be answering.'

The ARC's initiative has been widely welcomed. Stephen Holgate, who chairs the ARC's programme grant subcommittee, and is Professor of Immunopharmacology at the University of Southampton, is also heavily involved in the Foundation for Integrated Medicine.

The Foundation (whose President is Prince Charles) promotes just that – mainstream and complementary therapies working alongside each other. Its ideal would be a GP practice where patients are referred for acupuncture, homeopathy, osteopathy and massage therapy – all within the same centre and funded by the NHS. It's not a complete pipe-dream – a recent survey showed that 40 per cent of general practices provide access to complementary therapies, 70 per cent of which was funded by the NHS.

Stephen Holgate believes there are shortfalls in the provision of conventional treatments, and that there is scope for both doctors and qualified private practitioners to work side by side. But, he says, before that can happen there needs to be a proper training programme, and research to make sure complementary therapies are safe – as well as effective. A House of Lords Select Committee is looking to tighten up the regulations applying to complementary therapists to ensure they are all qualified and trained.

Dr Philip Helliwell, a rheumatologist and a member of the ARC's Education Committee, is cautiously enthusiastic about the charity's new move. His own rheumatology department offers patients acupuncture and manipulation, and refers them for chiropractic, osteopathy, and the Alexander technique.

'You could say that it's up to complementary therapists to prove the efficacy of what they practise, but on the other hand a lot of our patients use them, it morally behoves us to invest in them,' he says. 'Some therapies will doubtless be debunked, but unless we can come up with a terribly effective cure for their arthritis, people will keep on with these therapies.'

Professor Edzard Ernst, who heads the department of complementary therapies at the University of Exeter, and is a long-term advocate of the need for scientific evidence, warns that there has to be enough expertise available to make the initiative work.

'Lack of research skills and facilities means that an injection of funds is unlikely, in itself, to solve the problems of research into complementary therapies,' he says. 'A lack of research infrastructure has always been regarded as one major obstacle to the production of high-quality research.'

Dr George Lewith, honorary consultant physician at the University of Southampton's school of medicine, and author of the ARC's complementary therapies booklet, takes up the point.

'One of the main problems that exist within complementary medical research is the difficulty of encouraging new projects of high quality. Consequently, some ideas

that look very good do need mentoring. While there may be many ideas, the intellectual and research capacity to investigate them competently is limited.'

However, once the will is there, ways can usually be found. And to musculoskeletal physician at the University of Newcastle, Dr Susanne Bower, who is leading the ARC acupuncture trial, it's quite simple: 'Acupuncture requires credibility, and we want to produce an orthodox scientific study which will answer questions about efficacy and safety. If the study is positive towards acupuncture, then the medical establishment will take notice, and it will become accepted – and more widely available for the benefit of patients.'

Says Fergus Logan: 'What do we hope to achieve? Well, we don't yet know what response we will get from the complementary medicine movement, but we aim for an understanding of where things seem to work and why they do. And, just as important – we want spurious products and quackery to be debunked once and for all.'

• The above is an extract from the Arthritis Research Campaign's web site which can be found at www.arc.org.uk

© Arthritis Research Campaign

Homeopathy

Past, present and future medicine

What is homeopathy?

Homeopathy is a complete system of medicine. It is becoming popular again but it has been in world-wide use for nearly two hundred years.

The Royal Family has used it for generations. People suffering from all kinds of illnesses, from depression to arthritis, migraine to ulcers, and now the more 'modern' illnesses including AIDS and ME (myalgic encephalomyelitis), can be helped by homeopathy to regain their health.

Good homeopathy will not just

drive away the symptoms but help the patient deal with the cause of the illness and regain good health.

Homeopaths aim to help their patients achieve freedom from limitations in their lives, and, ideally, to reach a level of health where they are no longer dependent on any medicine or therapy.

Homeopathy is holistic medicine

The holistic approach to medicine takes a wider view of illness, a wider view of the causes of disease and the

ways in which people express their illness individually.

Paracelsus, a 16th century philosopher and physician, said, 'Those who merely study and treat the effects of disease are like those who imagine that they can drive away the winter by brushing the snow from the door. It is not the snow that causes winter, but the winter that causes the snow.'

Homeopaths do not treat physical, emotional and mental or even spiritual illnesses separately, but regard them as intimately connected, since all are aspects of the whole of the patient's suffering.

When starting homeopathic treatment, the patient may not realise the relevance of some of the questions being asked. It may appear that the homeopath is interested in matters which have little to do with the particular complaint about which the patient is most concerned.

Homeopaths understand that symptoms of illness are evidence of the body's natural and automatic efforts to heal itself and these clues are used to guide them when prescribing a homeopathic remedy.

In homeopathy more of these clues are used than in orthodox medicine, so the patient may be asked questions about all sorts of apparently minor deviations from health and about character and personality traits, in order to arrive at a clear understanding of the whole picture of the patient's state of health. Before prescribing, the homeopath wants to have a complete overview of the patient. The first consultation can take as long as two hours.

A remedy is then prescribed for that individual patient, not merely for his or her disease but for the person's whole state. Thus homeopathy is truly holistic. This fundamental principle of homeopathy, that of the individual prescription, explains why two patients with apparently similar illnesses may be treated with a different remedy. In other words, two patients might have headaches but the way they have their headaches can be different, their overall state of health can be different, the way they cope with life can be different and so on. To go back to the example from Paracelsus, you cannot drive away the whole illness by brushing the headache from the door!

Treating like with like, or the Law of Similars

Homeopathic remedies are prescribed according to the Law of Similars. This law states, 'That which makes sick shall heal.' This means that the symptoms caused by an overdose (too much) of a substance are the symptoms that can also be cured with a small dose of that substance.

For instance, we know that when cutting a strong onion we often experience an acrid runny nose, a particular soreness in the throat and stinging, runny eyes; so a homeopath will prescribe *Allium cepa* (the homeopathic remedy made from onion) for the patient who has a cold and bad throat with these particular symptoms.

Homeopaths sometimes simplify the Law of Similars by saying that they treat 'like with like'. The name homeopathy comes from the same idea. It is derived from two Greek words, meaning 'similar + suffering'. The Law of Similars has been a part of medical practice at least since the time of classical Greece, but homeopathy as we know it today was first formulated two hundred years ago by Samuel Hahnemann, a German physician, chemist and linguist.

What are homeopathic remedies?

The remedies which homeopaths use come from many different sources. Most are derived from plants, but minerals, metals and some poisons which have been used medicinally for generations are also used.

After initial preparation of the raw material the remedies are made by serial dilution and succussion (vigorous shaking) in a solution of alcohol and water. This is done a few (three to four) times or up to many thousands of times. The liquid dilution is then used itself as a remedy or soaked into tablets or granules for convenience.

The diluted remedies are described as being 'potentised', in recognition of the dynamic healing power they can stimulate.

How do homeopathic remedies work?

Frequently the dilution is so great that no chemical trace of the original substance remains but, if no chemical trace remains, how do the remedies work?

There is abundant proof that the remedies do work but homeopaths and scientists have yet to discover exactly why they work.

A precise answer is likely to be found outside the chemistry laboratory in the field of physics, especially electro-magnetism. The process of dilution and succussion apparently imprints the characteristic energy pattern, or blueprint, of the original substance onto the water in which it is diluted. This may be likened to the transmission of television signals, where the original scene is converted into an electro-magnetic energy pattern (a signal) which can then be broadcast to your receiver.

A homeopathic remedy acts as a signal which energises or stimulates the body's self-healing power, mobilising the defence systems and working on the mental, emotional and physical aspects of the body.

Homeopathy is gentle and subtle, or the principle of the minimum dose

In homeopathy, only one remedy (or signal) is used at a time. Just as a television reproduces only the programme to which it is tuned, so a sick person is very sensitive to, or 'tuned-in' to, the correct remedy and only a minute stimulus from the right signal (or remedy) is required. This is sometimes called the principle of the minimum dose. The idea is to cure with the minimum amount of medicine and the minimum of intervention.

It is the body's energy which is influenced rather than its chemical balance, and the remedies do not cause side-effects, as there is no chemical trace to accumulate in the body's tissues. For the same reasons it is not possible to take an overdose of homeopathic medicine in the same way as in orthodox medicine (orthodox medicine works on a chemical level).

Homeopathic medicines are not therefore intrinsically dangerous. Nonetheless, they are clearly capable of stimulating the body's reactive forces powerfully and should be treated with respect.

Research but no experiments on animals

Homeopathic remedies are tested on people, not on animals. Groups of volunteers under supervision take a safe dose, of a substance prepared as a homeopathic remedy, repeatedly over a period of time until they produce a range of symptoms. These symptoms of 'the proving' are carefully recorded. Additional information on the action of many homeopathic remedies has been gathered for over two hundred years, from clinical experience, and all the information is recorded precisely in two types of homeopathic reference book, the materia medica, and the repertory, as well as on computer.

This information is then used to prescribe a remedy for a patient with the same symptoms, according to the Law of Similars (that which makes sick shall heal).

There is much precision involved both in testing remedies

and prescribing them. Collective experience reinforces the understanding of their curative action and, because of the way in which they are prescribed, they are not made redundant (as are many chemical drugs) by 'new' or drug-resistant bacteria and viruses.

Is homeopathy the same as vaccination?

The Law of Similars (that which makes sick shall heal) principle of homeopathy is often compared to vaccination. Vaccines introduce a small amount of the weakened virus or bacterium related to a disease into the body in order to raise the body's immune response against that disease. However, homeopathy is quite different because homeopathic remedies are extremely diluted and therefore no diseased material (biological or chemical trace) is introduced into the body.

Another fundamental difference is that a homeopathic prescription is specific to that particular patient and stimulates the body's immune system to be strengthened against all illness, not just a single disease.

How the remedies are given

Remedies may be prescribed in a number of different strengths, or potencies as they are called. The lower potencies have been subjected to less dilution and succussion than the higher ones and are not, broadly speaking, as powerful and long-lasting in their effects. It is the low potencies such as the sixth (e.g.

Arnica 6) which are to be found on sale in many chemists and health food shops. High potency remedies are usually prescribed by experienced qualified homeopaths.

Remedies can be prescribed in different ways. Sometimes they are given as a single dose (probably in a high potency) when it is likely that homeopath and patient will wait for a period of weeks to see the patient's response. A remedy can also be given in a lower potency, singly or repeated daily or more frequently.

The homeopath will choose the method to suit the patient and the nature of the illness. For instance, a person who has been ill for a long time and whose body has been physically damaged may need repeated doses of a remedy to stimulate the recuperative powers, whereas a young and basically healthy person may respond very quickly to a single high potency remedy. Individual patients also respond better to some methods than others; understanding this is part of the skill of the homeopath and explains why attempts to prescribe for oneself may prove ineffective.

The individual prescription and the individual response

After taking a homeopathic remedy, different patients respond in different ways. While some feel an immediate surge of well-being such as they have rarely felt before, others may suddenly feel very tired at first and need to rest for a day or so before improvement – this often happens with patients who have been under stress and who really do need to stop and recuperate. Sometimes the original symptoms temporarily become worse, or patients may experience a brief awareness of symptoms of illnesses they have had in the past and from which they have not truly recovered. All these reactions are indications that the remedy is working and that a process of self-healing has begun. Sometimes these responses are quite subtle and may pass unnoticed, while at other times they can be quite marked.

What are self-healing powers?

Since medicine began it has been recognised that there is a capacity for self-healing within the human organism. In acute illnesses such as colds, chickenpox etc., the body naturally resists infection and, in time, gets better through mobilising its own defences, helped by rest, fresh air and the right food. In more long-lasting chronic illnesses, such as repeated migraine or depression, the body's vitality is often too depleted to do this without assistance. In these cases the right remedy will stimulate the body's self-healing powers to start the process of cure.

Over many years this self-healing power has been given various names in different cultures. It has been called prana in India, chi in China and the vital force in Europe. Researchers have attempted to localise it in what is called, in modern medical terminology, the immune system. It is not yet completely clear to anyone what exactly it is in us that heals disease, though we often see demonstrations of its power.

The potential of homeopathy

Health care everywhere is undergoing great change as many people realise that there is more to health than being physically fit and well fed. Innovative techniques in surgery and 'miracle' drugs improve many lives but continuing chronic illnesses, such as heart disease, arthritis, cancer, allergies, emotional and mental disturbance, are the fate of many more.

Homeopathy has a great deal to offer. With this different approach to illness, a homeopath can often help patients with diseases generally considered incurable by conventional medicine.

Homeopathy – medicine of the 21st century

Homeopathy also offers a method of maintaining health and preventing illness. It is a subtle but effective therapy that can correct small imbalances long before the appearance of the more serious symptoms which denote a particular disease. It is not necessary for a homeopath to wait for a conventional diagnosis before treatment can commence. Much illness can be 'nipped in the bud' and the patient swiftly restored to health before a more serious disease appears.

People who have had homeopathic treatment generally find that their state of health and well-being has improved. They are better able to resist infection and have a greater sense of stability and individual purpose in life. These improvements surely are steps towards real health.

How do I find a good homeopath?

To find a good homeopath consult the Register of the Society of Homeopaths. All homeopaths registered with the Society practise in accordance with a Code of Ethics and Practice, have professional insurance, and have passed stringent academic and clinical assessments before being admitted to the Register.

It is important that you feel happy with the manner and approach of your homeopath. In that way you will be more able to give your homeopath the information needed to prescribe well for you.

© *The Society of Homeopaths*

Reflexology

By Linda Dooley IIHHT, ICHT, Member of the Federation of Holistic Therapists

What is reflexology?

The ancient healing art of reflexology has been known to man for many thousands of years and was first practised by early Indian, Chinese and Egyptian people.

Dr William Fitzgerald, an American ear, nose and throat surgeon, introduced this therapy to the West in 1913. He noted that pressure on specific parts of the body could have an anaesthetising effect on a related area. Developing this theory, he divided the body into ten equal and vertical zones, ending in the fingers and toes. He concluded that pressure on one part of a zone could affect everything else within that zone. Thus, reflex areas on the feet and hands are linked to other areas and organs of the body within the same zone.

In the 1930s, a therapist called Eunice Ingham further developed and refined the zone therapy, into what is now known as foot reflexology. She observed that congestion or tension in any part of the foot mirrors congestion or tension in a corresponding part of the body. Thus, when you treat the big toes there is a related effect in the head, and treating the whole foot can have a relaxing and healing effect on the whole body.

How can reflexology help you?

The body has the ability to heal itself. Following illness, stress, injury or disease, it is in a state of imbalance, and vital energy pathways are blocked, preventing the body from functioning effectively. Reflexology can be used to restore and maintain the body's natural equilibrium and encourage healing.

A reflexologist uses hands only to apply gentle pressure to the feet. For each person the application and the effect of the therapy is unique. Sensitive, trained hands can detect tiny deposits and imbalances in the feet, and by working on these points the reflexologist can release blockages and restore the free flow of energy to the whole body. Tensions are eased, and circulation and elimination is improved. This gentle therapy encourages the body to heal itself at its own pace, often counteracting a lifetime of misuse.

Who can benefit from reflexology?

Since reflexology treats the whole person, not the symptoms of disease, most people benefit from treatment. The therapy brings relief to a wide range of acute and chronic conditions, and is suitable for all ages. Once your body is in-tune, it is wise to have regular treatments in order to help maintain health and well-being. An increasing number of people are using this safe, natural therapy as a way of relaxing, balancing and harmonising the body.

Please ensure that your practitioner is professionally qualified and a member of a bona fide organisation.

What happens when you go for treatment?

On your first visit there is a preliminary consultation with the practitioner. Your general health and recent medical history will be discussed. Because reflexology is a holistic therapy it is important that the therapist understands your body as a whole. Certain conditions might necessitate obtaining the agreement of your own GP before treatment can begin.

The reflexologist then begins to work on your feet, or hands if necessary, noting problem areas. There may be discomfort in some places, but it is fleeting, and is an indication of congestion or imbalance in a corresponding part of the body. For the most part, the sensation is pleasant and soothing. Reflexology will relax you while stimulating the body's own healing mechanisms.

A course of treatment varies in length depending on your body's needs and usually lasts for about one hour, although the initial consultation may add some time to your first visit. After the first treatment or two your body may respond in a very

definite way: you may have a feeling of well-being and relaxation; or you may feel lethargic, nauseous or tearful, but this is transitory. It is, however, vital information for reflexologists, as it shows how your body is responding to treatment. You might be asked to keep a note of your progress between treatments.

A vital part of any holistic treatment is cleansing of the body. This will involve the consumption of what you might consider abnormally large quantities of water to assist flushing toxins from your system.

• The above information is from the web site www.reflexology.org.uk

What is reflexology?

Reflexology is a form of 'alternative' or 'complementary' medicine and involves a method of treatment using massage to reflex areas found in the feet and the hands. Most commonly, the feet are used as the areas to be treated.

In the feet, there are reflex areas corresponding to all the parts of the body and these areas are arranged in such a way as to form a map of the body in the feet with the right foot corresponding to the right side of the body and the left foot corresponding to the left side of the body. By having the whole body represented in the feet, the method offers a means of treating the whole body and of treating the body as a whole. This latter point is an important factor of a natural therapy and allows not only symptoms to be treated but also the causes of symptoms.

The method has been used for several thousands of years and is known to have been practised in a similar manner by the Chinese and the Egyptians. More recently, reflexology was described in the form in which it is now known by the late Eunice Ingham, an American lady, who based her method of treatment on work called 'Zone Therapy' which had been described some years earlier in the 1920s by an American, Dr William Fitzgerald. The main pioneer of reflexology in Great Britain was the late Doreen Bayly who introduced the method in the early 1960s and whose great determination to stimulate awareness and interest in the method should not be forgotten.

Reflexology does not claim to be a 'cure-all' but numerous different disorders have been successfully treated by this method. These disorders include such things as migraine, sinus problems, hormonal imbalances, breathing disorders, digestive problems, circulatory problems, back problems and tension and stress. Most people who have experienced treatment would agree that the method can be most beneficial and is also a very relaxing therapy.

What is aromatherapy?

Information from the Register of Qualified Aromatherapists

Aromatherapy and essential oils

Aromatherapy is the holistic application of essential oils to improve physical and emotional well-being.

Essential oils are fragrant, volatile (quickly evaporating) liquids that occur naturally in the 'glands' of plants. They are extracted from flowers, leaves, seeds, roots, fruits and woods through distillation and expression. Essential oils that are commonly used in aromatherapy include lavender, geranium, bergamot, clary sage and sandalwood.

Essential oils have been used in perfumery, food flavouring and medicine for one thousand years. And long before they were first distilled in Persia the ancient Egyptians produced scented oils from frankincense, cedarwood and other plants — put to use by priest and perfumer alike.

Essential oils are highly concentrated and must be diluted before being applied. For use in massage they are mixed with a carrier such as almond, walnut or sunflower oil. Massage is one of the safest ways for the body to benefit from plant essences, as the skin absorbs oil rather slowly.

Each essential oil possesses distinct therapeutic properties that help to promote health and prevent disease. Supporting and harmonising both body and mind, they have been found to increase vitality, alleviate tension and fight infection. The ability of essential oils to have a calming or uplifting effect psychologically is directly linked to the effect of their wonderful aromas, involving the link between olfaction (smelling) and the brain.

Aromatherapy massage

In the practice of aromatherapy, essential oils are applied in a variety of ways including massage, ointments, lotions, baths and inhalations. Their holistic application is geared towards the needs of the individual. Aromatherapists know that each individual requires a unique blend of essences.

Combining the benefits of essential oils with those of therapeutic massage produces a deeply pleasurable yet highly effective way of healing. Together they enhance the circulation of blood and lymph, relax and tone tense, tired muscles, improve nervous conductivity, and promote an overall sense of well-being.

In our increasingly stressful, often impersonal world, massage is being rediscovered as a thoroughly renewing, non-invasive form of communication through touch.

Professional treatment

Your first visit to a professional aromatherapist will normally involve a consultation. Here they will ask you about your general health and vitality, medical history and emotional well-being. (All information will naturally be held in the strictest confidence.) Following this your aromatherapist will select and blend the essential oils appropriate for your individual needs and may apply them in combination with massage. Further visits require a shorter consultation time and may involve a slightly smaller fee.

Your aromatherapist may, with your consent, wish to write to your GP to inform him or her that you are receiving aromatherapy treatment. This is done mainly in the interests of establishing good relations with the medical profession. Your aromatherapist may also be qualified to practise other natural health disciplines such as reflexology, acupressure massage, touch for health and counselling.

© *The Register of Qualified Aromatherapists*

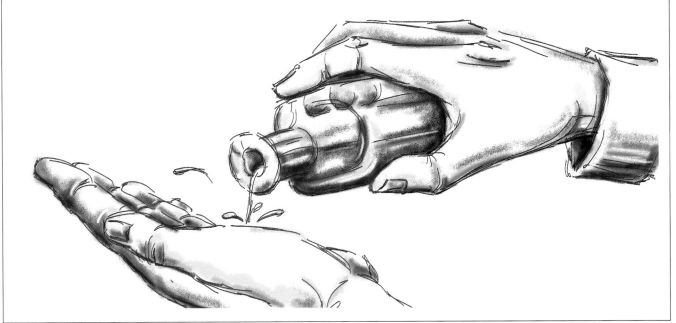

Acupuncture: an overview

Information from the British Medical Acupuncture Society (BMAS)

The general public has become increasingly interested in a wide variety of so-called 'alternative' therapies. These can range from the well established to the downright eccentric. One of those which has the most scientific research to support it is acupuncture. Although it has been used to treat a multiplicity of diseases for thousands of years, now its mechanisms of action are becoming understood it has gained scientific credibility in Western medicine. As a result of this, it has earned its reputation as a complementary rather than 'alternative' technique alongside conventional Western medicine.

Acupuncture is its own best advertisement – it works! Acupuncture can relieve symptoms which have not been helped by Western medicine. Satisfied patients tell their friends, and GPs may be asked to recommend an acupuncturist. Many patients are determined to 'try' acupuncture, whatever the attitude of their GP. Unless the practising doctor knows something about acupuncture and which conditions may be helped by it, a breakdown of doctor/patient communication may result, to the detriment of both. If they are not interested in using acupuncture themselves, they may wish to refer patients to practitioners whose expertise they can rely on. The British Medical Acupuncture Society is able to supply names of such qualified practitioners. Full membership of the Society is only open to those with a medical degree and GMC registration together with adequate training in acupuncture. Medically qualified acupuncturists will not hesitate to inform GPs if acupuncture does not seem to be the most appropriate form of treatment and will keep GPs in touch with the patient's progress. Referral to a medically qualified acupuncturist can protect the patient from the pitfalls of self-referral to a 'lay' practitioner.

Unfortunately, the upsurge in demand for non-drug treatments has been followed by a proliferation of practitioners in all therapies. Acupuncture is no exception and there is a wide range of training programmes for 'lay' acupuncturists. Registration is not compulsory, there is little quality control or accountability. Unlike the medically trained practitioners the 'lay' acupuncturist is permitted to advertise.

What is acupuncture?

The word acupuncture is derived from the Latin 'acus', needle, and 'punctura', to prick. Certain strategic points on the body are pierced with fine needles or stimulated with massage, heat or electricity. Through this, relief of symptoms can occur in areas close to the needles, or in distant parts of the body. Acupuncture is based on the nervous connection between the body's organs and its surface. When an organ is diseased, pain may be referred to points on or just under the skin. These may become tender and may be obvious to the patient, or he may only realise they are there when they are identified by the acupuncturist.

Stimulation of these and other non-tender acupuncture points, usually with fine needles, sends afferent impulses to the central nervous system and so influences the corresponding organ or other area of the body.

The Chinese describe about 1,000 acupuncture points which they divide into twelve groups, joined by imaginary lines on the body's surface called meridians. The meridians are associated with the internal organs such as the lung, large bowel and stomach.

Acupuncture: diagnosis

In traditional Chinese medicine, diagnosis was based on history, observation and examination of the tongue, confirmed by an elaborate pulse diagnosis. Nowadays, the medically trained acupuncturist approaches a patient in much the same way as any other physician. Diagnosis must precede treatment; so he takes a full medical history, followed by a careful medical examination. If the diagnosis is not obvious he may arrange special investigations such as x-rays.

Having made the diagnosis the medically qualified acupuncturist is in a position to choose the appropriate treatment for his patient – this may not be acupuncture. For example, medical acupuncturists would refer the patient with acute appendicitis to a surgeon.

Unfortunately, the acupuncturist who is not medically trained may not always recognise serious or potentially serious conditions which would be more appropriately treated in other ways. Inappropriate acupuncture treatment might mask a disease by alleviating a symptom such as pain; so the patient seeks conventional treatment at a later, less treatable stage.

The 'lay' acupuncturist is also less likely to have close links with doctors such as GPs and specialists who can contribute to diagnosis and care of the patient. Also he cannot provide other appropriate forms of treatment such as drugs or minor surgery.

Acupuncture: what it is used for

In the West acupuncture is used for a range of conditions rather arbitrarily, because of historical associations and assumptions rather than a scientifically valid programme of assessment of its efficacy. Some work has been carried out, and, further, studies are being undertaken which confirm or deny acupuncture's place in managing specific conditions. It is widely recognised to be effective in treating the following conditions:

- Musculoskeletal disorders such as fibromyalgia, tennis elbow, frozen shoulder, osteoarthritis
- Chronic pain states including some neuralgias
- Headaches including migraine
- Nausea and vomiting (post-operative, pregnancy, travel sickness, post-chemotherapy)
- Stress-related symptoms
- Asthma and allergic disorders such as nasosinusitis and eczema
- Certain bowel diseases including constipation and irritable bowel syndrome
- Withdrawal symptoms (tobacco, food, opiates, benzodiazepines)
- Premenstrual symptoms and minor gynaecological complaints

There are many other conditions such as hypertension or angina for which acupuncture may be beneficial. However it has so far not been possible to evaluate this as patients are not referred to practitioners for treatment, and effective drugs are available. Again, properly controlled clinical trials are required.

In further conditions such as infectious diseases, paralyses and malignancy there is less evidence of acupuncture's efficacy at present, as there are few clinical trials.

In view of the confusion in this area the doctor who does not practise acupuncture should consult a specialist in this technique in deciding whether it can help a given patient. Fortunately acupuncture has some decided advantages which will often suggest that a trial of therapy is justified: it is safe, cheap and can easily be combined with other treatment modalities such as drugs. In fact, whereas acupuncture may be unsuccessful alone in controlling some conditions, it may be beneficial in reducing the amount of drugs a patient has to take, such as opiods for the relief of chronic pain.

Acupuncture: how it is done

The skill of acupuncture is knowing where and how to stimulate the skin and subcutaneous structures in order to achieve the desired result. The acupuncture points are usually stimulated with needles – disposable or carefully sterilised to avoid the risk of HIV and hepatitis. Alternatively, an electric current is passed down a needle or the points stimulated via surface electrodes, by laser, heat or massage.

In manual acupuncture, the acupuncturist uses his skill to decide on the gauge of the needle, how to manipulate it, how deep to insert it, how long to leave it in place, and the frequency and number of treatments. Different needle manipulations, or different frequencies of electrical stimulation, have different therapeutic effects.

What the patient experiences

Treatment is usually painless although the patient may feel 'needling sensation' (so-called t'chi) which is a heavy dull aching feeling.

Indeed when this occurs it is often associated with a positive response.

Symptom relief is sometimes immediate. Other patients notice improvement over several days. Some need several treatments before they notice any improvement and of course some don't respond at all.

A sense of general well-being is very common. Some people feel elated after treatment; others feel very relaxed.

Side-effects are very uncommon. Fainting may occur rarely. Sometimes a temporary exacerbation of the disease being treated may be noticed. This almost always occurs with the first treatment only and may predict an eventual successful outcome.

Acupuncture: The British Medical Acupuncture Society

There is growing interest by the general public in all 'natural' forms of medicine. Unfortunately in the UK anyone is allowed to set up as an acupuncturist and treat patients. Medically qualified acupuncturists are, of course, accountable to the General Medical Council and will have professional indemnity insurance. Their prolonged professional training is a guarantee to patients of their knowledge of anatomy, physiology, diagnosis and the treatment of disease with techniques other than acupuncture. The British Medical Acupuncture Society was formed in 1980 to ensure that doctors are suitably trained before they practise acupuncture. Members include GPs, rheumatologists, anaesthetists, pain specialists and orthopaedic surgeons as well as dentists and veterinary surgeons.

The BMAS holds regular scientific meetings, encourages research, publishes a journal and runs training courses. It is affiliated to the International Council of Medical Acupuncture and Related Techniques whose membership is restricted to medical practitioners.

The BMAS opposes unfounded therapeutic claims and the practice and promotion of acupuncture by people lacking a medical background.
© British Medical Acupuncture Society (BMAS)

Osteopathy

Your questions answered (FAQs)

What is osteopathy?

Osteopathy is an established recognised system of diagnosis and treatment, which lays its main emphasis on the structural and functional integrity of the body. It is distinctive by the fact that it recognises that much of the pain and disability which we suffer stems from abnormalities in the function of the body structure as well as damage caused to it by disease.
(Description by General Osteopathic Council, 28 October 1998)

What kinds of problems can osteopathy help with?

Whilst back pain is the most common problem seen, osteopathy can help with a wide variety of problems including changes to posture in pregnancy, babies with colic or sleeplessness, repetitive strain injury, postural problems caused by driving or work strain, children with glue ear, the pain of arthritis and sports injuries among many others. Leaflets explaining many of the common treatments used are available from the Osteopathic Information Service.

Your local Registered Osteopath will be happy to advise as to whether they could help with your own particular problem.

What can I expect when I visit an osteopath?

When you visit an osteopath for the first time a full case history will be taken and you will be given an examination. You will normally be asked to remove some of your clothing and to perform a simple series of movements. The osteopath will then use a highly developed sense of touch, called palpation, to identify any points of weakness or excessive strain throughout the body.

The osteopath may need additional investigations such as x-ray or blood tests. This will allow a full diagnosis and suitable treatment plan to be developed for you.

How much do treatments cost?

Treatments are approximately £20-£30 for a 30-40-minute treatment session. Often the first session is longer and may cost more.

How many treatments will I need?

Osteopathy is patient centred, which means treatment is geared to you as an individual. Your osteopath should be able to give you an indication after your first visit. For some acute pain one or two treatments may be all that is necessary. Chronic conditions may need ongoing maintenance. An average is 6-8 sessions.

Do I need a referral from my GP?

A formal referral from your GP is not necessary, the majority of osteopathic patients self-refer.

How does osteopathy work?

Osteopaths work with their hands using a wide variety of treatment techniques. These may include soft tissue techniques, rhythmic passive joint mobilisation or the high velocity thrust techniques designed to improve mobility and the range of movement of a joint. Gentle release techniques are widely used, particularly when treating children or elderly patients. This allows the body to return to efficient normal function.

How can I be sure I am in safe hands when visiting an osteopath?

A Registered Osteopath has demonstrated to the General Osteopathic Council via a detailed application process that they are a safe and competent practitioner, that they have adequate malpractice insurance and have agreed to abide by a Code of Practice.

I have noticed many osteopaths have the letters DO and/or BSc (Ost) after their names – what does this mean?

These are osteopathic qualifications. The DO stands for diploma in osteopathy the BSc is a degree in osteopathy. The length of training is the same for both, at least four years' full-time training. The diploma course has been around the longest but recently some courses have been validated by universities allowing them to offer their students degree passes.

Can I have osteopathic treatment on the NHS?

Most people consult an osteopath

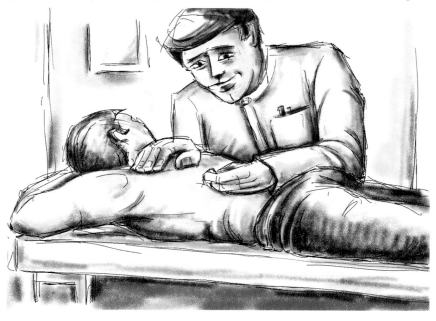

privately. Telephone local practices to find out about fees in your area. An increasing number of osteopaths work with GP practices so that it may be possible for your doctor to refer you to an osteopath on the NHS.

Can I have osteopathy on my private medical insurance?

Many private health insurance schemes give benefit for osteopathic treatment. Some companies will reimburse the total fee or pay a percentage of the costs. Contact the helpline of your insurance company who will explain the actual benefits and methods of claim for your individual policy.

What should I do if I am unhappy with my osteopathic treatment?

Often problems are caused by misunderstandings and can easily be resolved by discussing your concerns with the osteopath directly. If this does not resolve the problem or your concerns are of a more serious nature the GOsC has a Code of Practice which patients may refer to.

Whilst back pain is the most common problem seen, osteopathy can help with a wide varied of problems

---

What is the status of osteopathy in the UK?

The 1993 report from the British Medical Association *Complementary Medicine – New Approaches to Good Practice* recognised osteopathy as a discrete clinical discipline. Osteopathy is the first complementary health care profession to be accorded statutory regulation (Osteopaths Act 1993).

More on statutory regulation

This legislation came into force on 9 May 2000 requiring all osteo-paths to be registered with the GOsC.

What are the origins of osteopathy?

Andrew Taylor Still, born in 1828 in Virginia, USA, trained as a doctor according to the system of medical education available at the time. As time went on he followed a different path from many of his peers, eschewing alcohol and the habit of contemporary physicians of administering crude drugs at their disposal in heroic quantities. This drove him to seek new methods of treating sickness. The outcome of his research was the application of physical treatment as a specialised form of treatment for which he coined the name 'Osteopathy'.

In 1892 A. T. Still organised a school in Kirksville, Missouri, for the teaching of osteopathy and it was from these small beginnings that osteopathy was brought to the UK around the turn of the century. The first school of osteopathy in the UK was set up in London in 1917 and over time other schools and colleges followed.

Today there are around 3,000 osteopaths in the UK performing over six million patient consultations a year.

© General Osteopathic Council

Iridology

A diagnostic method based on medical research

Iridology is the study of the irises of the eye, that is, the exposed nerve endings which make up the coloured part of the eye, all of which are connected to the brain. On a parallel with reflexology, where the practitioner can feel the abnormalities of the reflex nerve endings, a trained iridologist can actually see a veritable Ordinance Survey map of the reflex nerve endings exposing genetic inheritance, congestive and irritative zones and their various inter-reactions, within the bodily systems. In the hands of those who are well versed in the pathology of the pathways of disease, as well as anatomy and physiology, this provides a veritable microchip of information.

Iridology complements all therapeutic sciences because it provides the vital information needed in order to establish the root

---

By Angela Bradbury FGNI, MBRI, ND, D.Hom.

---

cause of ailments, thus revealing the appropriate treatments required. Hippocrates and Philostratus used iridology. Iridology was taught at the Medical School of Salerno and even the Chaldeans of Babylonia, in 1000 BC, left records of iride markings, with the relevant anatomical reflexes painted onto stone slabs.

In the 17th, 18th and 19th centuries, writings and works on iris markings and their meanings were recorded, largely by medical practitioners. One of the earliest was Dr Ignatz von Peczely, a Hungarian doctor. When he was 11 years old, he accidentally broke the leg of an owl when it instinctively fought against being captured. The boy noticed a black mark appearing in the owl's iris as victor and captor glared at each other. As von Peczely nursed the owl back to health, and in the following years of a more voluntary relationship, he noticed the mark which appeared upon injury, changing in form and shading.

Ignatz von Peczely qualified in medicine in 1867 at the Vienna medical college. During his internship he had ample opportunity to study the irises of patients before and after surgery. He also performed innumerable autopsies and, throughout, researched, systematically, his earlier findings, correlating and extending his knowledge, before publishing his book *Discoveries in the Realms of Nature and Art of Healing*, establishing his Iris Chart, in 1880.

Meanwhile, in the 1860s, a Swedish boy, Nils Liljequist, was reduced from a robust young man to a sickly boy as a result of vaccination, followed by much drugging with quinine and iodine. Between the ages of 14 and 20, he noted the changes in the colour of his formerly blue eyes, as the drug spots accumulated. In 1870 he published a paper, *Quinine and iodine change the colour of the iris*. Changing his career pathway from that of allopathic medicine, Liljequist, became a homeopath, as that was the treatment which restored him. After studying many of his patients, he published *Om Oegendiagnosen* in 1893, which included his iris chart. Human anatomy being what it is, we should not be surprised that both his chart and von Peczely's were so similar.

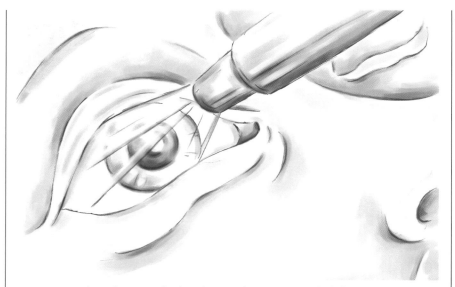

Much of the American medical research stemmed from the Austrian émigré, Dr Henry Edward Lane, who carried out most of his surgical and autopsy correlations with iride markings at the Kosmos Sanatorium in Evanston, Illinois. His book, *Iridology. The diagnosis from the eye*, was published in 1904 as *The Scientific Essay for the Public and Medical Profession*, and he substantiates his record with the fact that 'thousands were examined before just one marking could be considered corroborated'.

One of Dr Lane's students was Henry Lindlahr, MD, the champion of 'the healing crises'. He, too, became a surgeon, and amongst his vast written works, placing nature cures onto a scientific basis, in 1919, he published *Iridiognosis and Other Diagnostic Methods*.

The well-known writings of Bernard Jensen, DC, ND, Ph.D., stem from his photographic and medically corroborated research. He had studied under Dr Lindlahr and also worked for two nights a week for four years at the International School of Professional Arts and Sciences, in San Francisco, California, with the Chiropractor, R.M. McLain, on an intensive study and investigation into using iridology as a means of analysing patients' problems. Jensen states, in his book *Iridology. The Science and Practice of the Healing Arts. Volume 11*, that 'Dr McLain proved conclusively that iridology

was practical and scientific by the beneficial results he achieved with patients.'

Dr J. Haskel Kritzer recorded his lifetime of research into iris diagnosis in his textbook *Iridiagnosis*, soon to be republished by the Holistic Health College, London. It was his work which spurred Bernard Jensen on to further research, developing a more up-to-date iris chart, along with a colleague of Dr Kritzer, Dr John R. Arnold, founder of the World Iridology Fellowship. Dr Arnold insisted on the scientific exactness of any research before it could be considered valid. He was the main instigator in changing the term 'iridiagnosis' to 'iris analysis', which more accurately reflects that it is a means of analysing conditions within rather than specific diseases.

Dr V. L. Fernandiz, a medical and naturopathic physician, in Barcelona, Spain, published, in 1970, a comprehensive work, *Iridodiagnosis*, clearly illustrating how valuable early diagnosis was, from the iris, before pathological states advance enough to be clinically diagnosed. He stated that 'the great advantage of iridology to medical

---

Iridology complements all therapeutic sciences because it provides the vital information needed in order to establish the root cause of ailments

---

doctors is its reliability as an indicator of the early stages of disease, allowing many more lives to be saved'.

There are many more researchers who deserve acknowledgement, such as the Germans, Josef Deck, Theodor Kriege, Josef Angerer, Dr H. W. Schimmeland, Dr Rudolf Schnable, to name but a few. There is a great deal of intensive research and writings on iridology, but we have concentrated here on the medicos. For the benefit of those who have not had a chance to investigate the enormous amount of scientific research, involving millions of case histories, worldwide research, utilising surgery, autopsy, x-ray, scanning and chemical analysis, in Russia, Germany, New Zealand, Australia, Canada, America, South America and Europe, we trust this synopsis will clarify matters on the optic-neuro reflexed information provided by over 2800 exposed nerve endings. Just as the vascular system, exposed in the posterior of the inner eye, is most revealing, so are the autonomic and central nerve system exposures.

Today, iridology is part of the curriculum in the medical schools in Moscow, the Bobigy Faculty of Medicine at the University of Paris Nord, and various Egyptian and Greek medical schools. It is used, worldwide, by natural medicine practitioners and we, today, have even more extensive scientific resources for the ever continuing corroboration of our findings.

© *Holistic Health Consultancy London*

The Natural Medicines Society

Some questions answered

Are natural medicines safe?

We often hear '. . . they are natural, therefore, they are safe . . .', yet you wouldn't go into the garden and eat, for example, Deadly Nightshade (Belladonna) or Foxglove (Digitalis). However, generally speaking many of the substances used in natural medicines are not intrinsically dangerous, but it is important to remember that any substance capable of having a physiological effect on the mind or body should, as with any medicines, be treated with respect. Any dosage directions given, whether on the packaging or by the practitioner, should be followed properly.

Alternative and complementary medicines, like orthodox medicines, are not a 'cure-all', but they have the potential to improve health and strengthen resistance to illness and many offer an effective, safer form of treatment than drugs.

How do natural medicines work?

Although there is more research being conducted, most of this is geared to whether the medicine is effective in treating specific conditions. Scientists have yet to agree, for example, on how homoeopathic or anthroposophical medicines work.

One theory, for homoeopathy, is that the answer could be found in the field of physics, especially electromagnetism, rather than through chemistry. The dilution and succussion process is said by some to imprint an energy pattern, or blueprint, of the original substance onto the dilutent used. Potentised medicines are said to act as a signal which stimulates the individual's self-healing powers, mobilising the defence system to work on the mental, emotional and physical aspects of the patient.

Researchers have attempted to localise it in what is called, in modern medical terminology, the immune system. It is not yet completely clear to anyone what exactly it is in us that heals disease, although demonstrations of its efficacy have been seen.

Do animals have to be used for research?

There are techniques that can be used instead of animal experimentation to measure safety and efficacy of natural medicines, and organisations such as the Dr Hadwen Trust for Humane Research are constantly working to develop new methodology.

The majority of manufacturers and practitioners of natural medicines (and a growing number of consumers) believe that the use of animals to test natural medicines is inappropriate and unethical. Some 'flagship' trials, using patient selection, to prove the principle of homoeopathy have been undertaken over the past few years and medical outcome studies are increasingly being used to evaluate both medicines and therapies.

How do I know which therapy to choose?

Once you have decided to try an alternative approach to health care, deciding which particular therapy to use is probably the most difficult of decisions. Knowing the options for treating particular conditions, which treatments are available or useful, what the treatment involves or what to expect when consulting the practitioner – the many questions raised can be daunting, but, if you have committed yourself to a new approach you will either know something already, however little, or absolutely nothing at all about alternative treatments. If the former, then you may already have an idea of which therapy you wish to choose, if the latter, then the best way to understand the different approaches is perhaps to check at your local library and look through some of the books on alternative treatments. Once you have short-listed the approaches you would like to try, we would recommend that you contact the professional organisation representing the particular therapies and ask them for further information. From this, you should be able to decide in which direction you wish to go.

• The above is an extract from the Natural Medicines Society (NMS) web site which can be found at www.thenms.demon.co.uk

© The Natural Medicines Society (NMS)

The Register of Chinese Herbal Medicine

What is Chinese Herbal Medicine?

Health is more than just the absence of disease, and Chinese Medicine recognises this with its unique capacity for enjoyment, fulfilment and happiness.

Chinese Herbal Medicine (CMH) is an ancient system of health care that has undergone continual development over the centuries as the causes of illness that afflict mankind have evolved. This process continues today with the development of modern medical diagnostic tech-niques and knowledge. In its country of origin it is not an alternative form of therapy, but is used in the state hospitals alongside modern medicine.

Chinese Medicine includes all Oriental traditions emanating from south-east Asia that originally derived in China. Practitioners may work within a tradition which comes from Japan, Vietnam, Taiwan or Korea.

Chinese Medicine is a complete medical system that is capable of treating disease in all its forms. Although your practitioner will treat whatever complaint you have come for, the traditional view places great importance on preventative medicine, with the emphasis being on 'the disease that has not happened yet'; to diagnose and treat illness before it occurs.

Chinese Medicine consists of:

- herbal therapy
- acupuncture
- dietary therapy
- exercise
- lifestyle management.

Some or several of these may be employed in the course of treatment.

What are the herbs like and how much will they cost?

Herbs are now available in a number of formats, both traditional and modern. The traditional method is to boil a mixture of dried herbs to make a tea or to use pills. The herbs are now also commonly prescribed as freeze dried powders or tinctures. The herbs will certainly taste unusual at first to anyone who has not tried them before, but the vast majority of people get used to the taste very quickly.

There are no standard prices for treatment or herbs. This will depend on the individual practitioner and the part of the country you are in. You should enquire about charges when making your appointment. Many private health insurance companies are now covering acupuncture and a few will also pay for herbal treatment. You should contact your insurance company to check.

Endangered species

The RCHM is greatly concerned about the threat to wild animals and plants that has come about as a result of the growth in demand for traditional medicines. We have a strict policy prohibiting the use of any type of endangered species by any of our Members and we work with the authorities to stop the trade in illegal substances wherever it is found.

What can Chinese Medicine treat?

Chinese Medicine can understand and treat all forms of ill health. The results that can be expected and the length of treatment required will depend on the severity of the disease, its duration and the general health of the patient. Chinese Herbal Medicine is probably most renowned in the West for its effects on:

- skin disease
- gynaecology
- digestive complaints
- respiratory conditions
- allergies
- disorders of the immune system
- pain
- psychological problems
- children's diseases
- addiction.

Who can have treatment?

Chinese Herbal Medicine can be employed by people of any age or constitution. Your practitioner will take any previous or current illness or medication into account before providing treatment. Children and pregnant women can be, and commonly are, cared for by Chinese Herbal Medicine.

• For an information pack including details of your nearest Member of the RCHM, please send a cheque or postal order for £2.50 made out to: The Register of Chinese Herbal Medicine, PO Box 400, Wembley, Middlesex, HAD 9NZ. Tel: 07000 790332. E-mail: herbmed@rchm.co.uk Web site: www.rchm.co.uk

© The Register of Chinese Herbal Medicine (RCHM)

Herbal medicine

A caring profession

What is herbal medicine?

Herbal medicine is the use of plant remedies in the treatment of disease. It is the oldest form of medicine known. Our ancestors, by trial and error, found the most effective local plants to heal their illnesses. Now, with the advancement of science enabling us to identify the chemical constituents within these plants, we can better understand their healing powers.

Herbalism, in this country, is now classed as an 'alternative' or 'complementary' discipline but it is still the most widely practised form of medicine worldwide with over 80% of the world's population relying on herbs for health.

The herbalist's approach

Medical herbalists are trained in the same diagnostic skills as orthodox doctors but take a more holistic approach to illness. The underlying cause of the problem is sought and, once identified, it is this which is treated, rather than the symptoms alone. The reason for this is that treatment or suppression of symptoms will not rid the body of the disease itself. Herbalists use their remedies to restore the balance of the body thus enabling it to mobilise its own healing powers.

The first consultation will generally take at least an hour. The herbalist will take notes on the patient's medical history and begin to build a picture of the person as a whole being. Healing is a matter of teamwork with patient, practitioner and the prescribed treatment all working together to restore the body to health.

Treatment may include advice about diet and lifestyle as well as the herbal medicine.

The second appointment may follow in two weeks, subsequent ones occurring monthly – this will depend on the individual herbalist, the patient and the illness concerned.

How do herbs work?

People have always relied on plants for food to nourish and sustain the body. Herbal medicine can be seen in the same way. Plants with a particular affinity for certain organs or systems of the body are used to 'feed' and restore to health those parts which have become weakened. As the body is strengthened so is its power and ability to fight off disease and when balance and harmony are restored, health will be regained.

What are the differences between pharmaceutical and herbal drugs?

Many of the pharmaceutical drugs used today are based on plant constituents and, even now, when scientists are seeking new 'cures' for disease it is to the plant world that they turn. They find, extract and then synthesise in the laboratory a single active constituent from the plant (the active constituent is the part of the plant that has a therapeutic value), this can then be manufactured on a large scale.

Herbal drugs, however, are extracts from a part of the whole plant (e.g. leaves, roots, berries etc.) and contain hundreds, perhaps thousands of plant constituents.

Herbalists believe that the active constituents are balanced within the plant and are made more (or less) powerful by the numerous other substances present. For example, the herb Ephedra sinica is the source of the alkaloid ephedrine which is used, in orthodox medicine, to treat asthma and nasal congestion but it has the side-effect of raising blood pressure. Within the whole plant are six other alkaloids one of which prevents a rise in blood pressure. Synthetic diuretics (drugs that increase the flow of urine) seriously reduce the potassium level in the body, this has to be restored using potassium supplements. The herbalist uses dandelion leaves which are a potent diuretic but contain potassium to naturally replace that which is lost.

What can herbal medicine treat?

Herbal medicine can treat almost any condition that patients might take to their doctor. Common complaints seen by herbalists include skin problems such as psoriasis, acne and eczema, digestive disorders such as peptic ulcers, colitis, irritable bowel syndrome and indigestion. Problems involving the heart and circulation like angina, high blood pressure, varicose veins, varicose ulcers etc. can also be treated successfully as can gynaecological disorders like premenstrual syndrome and menopausal problems, also conditions such as arthritis, insomnia, stress, migraine and headaches, tonsillitis, influenza and allergic responses like hayfever and asthma. Qualified herbalists know when a condition is best seen by a doctor or another therapist.

What is healing?

Information from the Institute for Complementary Medicine

'The cure of the part should not be attempted without treatment of the whole. No attempt should be made to cure the body without the soul. Let no one persuade you to cure the head until he has first given you his soul to be cured, for this is the great error of our day, that physicians first separate the soul from the body.'   (Plato)

'Complementary' means to 'complete'. Patients are helped back to 'wholeness' using physical, mental, emotional, vital force and spiritual dimensions of treatment. This approach remains generally in line with the thinking of Plato.

'Wholeness' means that the physical, mental, emotional and vital force are all in balance between themselves and with the spiritual consciousness known as the Soul. The body is, or should be, an expression of the Soul. Healing is the natural way in which all imbalances are rectified so that the symptoms of the stress or illness can be controlled. Sometimes our own natural ability to heal ourselves cannot cope so we need the help of others. Drugs may help in the short term but healing happens separately and this is why it is important to understand the process so that patients can help themselves back to health.

Healing is the act of getting rid of all the imbalances and creating harmony with the Soul. Consequently, Complementary Medicine is patient centred.

'I am not my body – I live in my body.'

Plato's quote still embodies the best explanation of why the split has occurred between current orthodox medicine and the traditional or complementary approaches. But this does not explain the reality and, if you would like to reason out the problem, the following examples may help.

This is another way of expressing Plato's vision. The physical body is ultimately controlled by the mind

and Soul consciousness. During our lifetime on Earth, our computer-like brain is programmed by every experience we have so that we react to external forces like threats, anger, danger or beauty, compassion and love. Each reaction of the mind has a direct influence on the physical body which responds in the way it has been programmed. Sometimes that programming is wrong which prevents the body's defence mechanism from functioning correctly. This allows illness and disease to get a foothold.

Perhaps the best example to explain this is to compare the motor car and driver with the human body.

A car has a framework which includes all the working parts plus seats for the passenger and a place for baggage. The driver decides what route, speed and direction is going to be taken. A car needs petrol for the engine, sparking plugs to ignite the fuel and a battery to spark the plugs. It is the driver who acts to avoid accidents and decides when the car needs servicing. It is the driver who must decide what fuel to use since putting ordinary fuel in a car which is programmed for unleaded will cause breakdown. Without any or all of these working parts the car will not go. Thus the driver has the overall responsibility of seeing the car is maintained and driven both safely and correctly

The ancients viewed humans as being constructed in much the same way. The physical part of us is represented by the car while the driver is considered as the vital force (car battery) and the spirit (Soul consciousness which decides motivation, direction and ethics). The old traditional systems of medicine accepted the vital force and spirit and treatments were for the healing energies which touched both the vitality and Soul to bring them back into harmony with the physical body.

Again, using the example of the car, we can begin to see the importance of correct thinking, motivation and nourishment as being means to maintaining health in the fullest sense. Healing is the equivalent of 'jump starting' the vital force similar to coping with a flat battery. But healing also helps the patient to recognise past problems and re-programme themselves towards health and well-being.

The healing process

Complementary Medicine is a system of medicine which treats the physical, mental, emotional and vitality of the patient together with the spirit. This central view runs through a variety of disciplines which traditionally work towards the same goal where harmony between all levels of consciousness including the vital force and spirit must be achieved if true healing is to happen.

Healing the whole person has traditionally been seen as part of a co-ordinated programme of treatment. However, the scientific approach has tended to separate the treatment of the symptoms from treatment of the cause. Science does not recognise the common factor which unites all traditional medical approaches, i.e. the vitality or spirit of the patient. Vital force and spirit can be equated with Chi in Chinese Medicine, Shakti in Indian Medicine, vital force in homoeopathy, etc.

The healing mechanism

This is difficult to evaluate. Healers channel this energy to the patient. The process begins with a sense of compassion felt by the healer for the one in distress. Mothers feel this sense for their children and 'kiss the hurt better' or gently 'stroke' the pain away. Every aspects of the mother's thought, physical, mental, emotional and spiritual energy is concentrated on helping her child to over come the pain. In terms of healing energy, the mother's vital force and spiritual senses are focused on helping the child to regain its balance and overcome distress.

Does the healer try to heal the symptom or seek to help the patient come to terms with the cause of the problem? It is not always easy to establish the primary need. In an ideal world both conditions need help and this is why the healer's prayer is usually on the following lines – 'May this patient receive the healing that they need.' In this way, the appropriate energies are drawn from the healer in such a way as to begin the process of regaining the overall balance between all levels of consciousness. The process is not usually very fast and the healer will need to help the patient to realise

that as it probably took a considerable time for the illness to develop so it will take time for the body to remove it.

The attitude of the patient

The way the patient views their problem is crucial and every attempt must be made to ensure that there is a balance between accepting the nature of the problem and expecting healing to occur.

This is especially important if the condition is life-threatening. There is a need to remain quietly confident that the healing processes will stimulate both the body's immune response and the determination to change, which must remain upper-most in the patient's mind. Recognising the possible cause of the illness is useful where it is possible to change but it must be recognised that dwelling on past mistakes can inhibit the healing. It is better to look at today as the first one of the rest of your life. By living in the present, it is possible to focus on a programme of healing which will build for the future and automatically remove problems from the past at a pace which the patient can manage without adding additional trauma.

Working with healers

There is a tendency for the public to think of healers as ordinary folk who have a natural gift. This gift can be from God, Nature or the Universe according to the individual belief and they give their services by the laying on of hands or prayer. Healing is certainly a gift which can be used by everyone but it is also a central part of all the ancient traditional medical treatments.

Healing energy is central to all those practitioners in Complementary Medicine. In homoeopathy, osteopathy, chiropractic, herbal medicine, aromatherapy, acupuncture and the other systems listed by the Institute for Complementary Medicine, the practitioner diagnoses and heals at all levels of consciousness. However, it is a fact that many have tried to remove the concept of healing energy from the training and focus on a more simple and symptomatic approach. Osteopathy is an example where a partially qualified practitioner may only be concerned with the structure of the body and pay little attention to the mental, emotional and spiritual health of the person. In these cases, a complete removal of the symptoms may not be easy to achieve. Joints may be realigned but the change is often not permanent because the cause has not been treated. The patient is always required to play a crucial part in their treatment but some cannot find the strength of purpose to make necessary changes in their lifestyle and belief systems to allow healing to reach its full potential.

© 2000 ICM (*Institute for Complementary Medicine*)

Healing and medicine

Information from the Doctor-Healer Network

Introduction

Healing – often known as spiritual healing or therapeutic touch – is a skill with a recorded history of over four thousand years. Misunderstood and under-exploited, it is a natural phenomenon which in use is profoundly relaxing, restorative and completely non-invasive. It can be of therapeutic value in a wide range of physical and psychological difficulties, sometimes to a remarkable degree, and it can be employed by itself or in conjunction with any other therapy.

The treatment

Healing involves a transfer of energy between the therapist and the patient to deal with stress, aid the patient's immune system and enable his or her self-healing mechanism to work with a problem in whatever way is naturally appropriate. In simple terms the body 'knows' how to deal with a broken bone or a cut finger and it is this natural ability to repair itself that the healer seeks to stimulate. The treatment is accomplished by concentrating on the patient with focused intent and by panning the hands at varying distances above the surface of the body. Sometimes light touch is employed. The resulting interaction of energy between the healer and the patient enables the depleted energy of the patient to benefit from the energy radiated by or through the healer.

Both the healer and patient usually experience a variety of physical sensations indicating that a process is indeed taking place, with a strong sense of being relaxed or revitalised on the part of the patient.

Therapeutic effect and the scientific evidence

Healing is a powerful natural relaxant and a powerful restorative. It has been proven scientifically to bring about a beneficial effect on stressed or damaged enzymes, seeds, yeasts, bacteria, plants and animals and to accelerate the healing of simple injuries in humans. In a review of over 150 controlled studies of healing more than half demonstrated significant effects.

With illnesses of a more complex nature in human beings scientific proof has been more difficult to establish because the benefit derived from healing can vary according to the ability of the healer, the patient's condition and the rapport between them.

In simple terms the body 'knows' how to deal with a broken bone or a cut finger and it is this natural ability to repair itself that the healer seeks to stimulate

---

In medicine a specific treatment is prescribed to produce a specific outcome. Healing works differently. Healing seeks to trigger a spontaneous reaction within the body which helps the natural self-healing mechanism to address malfunction at all levels more effectively. As a consequence the patient often experiences benefit in ways other than or in addition to any effect on the presenting symptom or injury itself.

Research over three years in a GP practice in South Devon using general and mental health questionnaires has yielded promising results including reduced attendances at surgery, a high level of patient satisfaction and a significant reduction in drugs bills. Exeter University's Department of Complementary Medicine has investigated healing with the support of a substantial grant from the Wellcome Trust and research is also being carried out into the effect of healing on the molecular structure of water. Further research projects are in prospect.

Experience over many years suggests that healing can be remarkably effective with a wide range of illnesses and injuries, both physical and psychological. Leaving aside the question of scientific research, the most effective test for healing is self-evidence: to see its effect on a patient or to experience it oneself.

Contra-indications

Healing is completely natural and has no undesirable side-effects. However it may result in the release of suppressed symptoms affecting the pattern of the patient's recovery, in simple terms 'feeling worse' before feeling better. This is something a doctor should be aware of and be prepared to monitor and investigate if necessary as part of his supervisory role in the treatment of the patient. For example an increase in pain might be indicative of a condition which calls for medical intervention and an abreaction might indicate a need for counselling.

Healers

Whilst many successful healers continue to work informally, training programmes are now offered by members of the Confederation of Healing Organisations and others which give healers a grounding for work in a medical setting including professional ethics, practice administration, elementary anatomy and physiology, listening and communication skills, record maintenance, issues around confidentiality and onward referral, meaningful observation of a client's condition and so on. In anticipation of governments' future regulation of complementary therapists, these organisations require of members a high and improving standard of training, adherence to a strict Code of Conduct and mandatory professional indemnity insurance cover.

© Doctor-Healer Network

Reiki

Information from the Reiki Association

Reiki (pronounced Ray-key) is a Japanese word meaning Universal Life Energy, an energy which is all around us.

Natural healing

Reiki is the name given to a system of natural healing which evolved from the experience and dedication of Dr Mikao Usui, a Professor of Theology who lived in Japan in the last century. Dr Usui developed this healing system from ancient Buddhist teachings after many years of study, research and meditation. He spent the rest of his life practising and teaching Reiki. Today Reiki continues to be taught by Reiki Masters who have trained in the tradition passed down from Master to student.

There is no belief system attached to Reiki so anyone can receive or learn to give a Reiki treatment, the only prerequisite is the desire to be healed.

A Reiki treatment

The method of receiving a Reiki treatment from a practitioner is a very simple process. The recipient simply lies on a couch and relaxes. If they are unable to lie down, the treatment can be given in a sitting position, the main thing is for the recipient to be as comfortable as

---

Reiki principles

Just for today
Do not worry

Just for today
Do not anger

Honour your parents,
teachers and elders

Earn your living honestly

Show gratitude
to every living thing

---

possible. There is no need to remove any clothing as Reiki will pass through anything, even plaster casts. The practitioner gently places their hands non-intrusively in a sequence of positions which cover the whole body. The whole person is treated rather than specific symptoms. A full treatment usually takes 1 to $1\frac{1}{2}$ hours with each position held for several minutes.

Which conditions can Reiki help?

It is possible to heal at any level of being: physical, mental, emotional or spiritual. Acute injuries can be helped to heal very quickly but more chronic illness takes longer. In some cases such as terminal illness, there is not enough time for the progress of

the disease to be reversed. However, in such cases there is usually great benefit and enhancement of the quality of life, giving a sense of peace and acceptance during the time remaining.

Reiki healing can be given anywhere at any time as no special equipment is needed. The practitioner is a channel which the energy is drawn through by the need or imbalance in the recipient. Neither person has to use any effort of will or concentration during this process.

As running water smoothes the jagged edges of a rock until it is small enough to roll away, Reiki flows to the areas of need, soothing pain and supporting the body's natural ability to heal itself.

Reiki supports all forms of treatment both orthodox and complementary.

Learning Reiki

The gift of Reiki can be attained in 2-4 consecutive days. Students attending a First Degree Reiki course will be initiated, or attuned, to the energy by a Reiki Master who will also teach a sequence of hand positions for treating oneself and other people. How to treat animals and plants will also be taught.

Reiki restores balance in one's life.
© The Reiki Association

Healing the emotions

By Stefan Ball, Author and Consultant at the Dr Edward Bach Centre

A great many people have heard of Rescue Remedy, which is used by all sorts of people to cope with crises and everyday emergencies: Princess Anne and Elizabeth Hurley are two of its better-known users. But how many know about the 38 individual flower remedies that are part of the same system of medicine, a system unusual in that it is aimed at treating the emotions rather than their physical manifestations?

Dr Edward Bach, MB, BS, MRCS, LRCP, DPH, was a well-known bacteriologist, pathologist and homoeopath whose career took him from University College Hospital to the London Homoeopathic Hospital and a successful Harley Street practice. His orthodox researches culminated in a series of oral vaccines that are still known as the seven Bach nosodes, but even though this work received great acclaim Bach himself was not satisfied. He wanted to replace the vaccines with plant material which he felt would be more effective. To this end he began experimenting in 1928 with medicines made from flowers.

Bach had always been more interested in the people suffering disease than in the diseases themselves – a fact that made him unusual at that time. But his work with the flower remedies convinced him that true health could only be maintained by treating the individual personality instead of concentrating exclusively on the diseases of the body. He found that by selecting flower remedies according to the personality and emotional states of individuals he was able to resolve these imbalances, and that well-balanced people got better physically because their bodies were quite literally free to heal themselves.

By the time he died in 1936 Dr Bach had discovered the 38 remedies that were needed to treat every possible emotional state, with each individual remedy being aimed at a particular emotion or characteristic. Sometimes people find it strange that only 38 can deal with everything, but in fact used in combination over 292 million different mental states are covered by these 38 'primary' remedies, which are:

- Agrimony for people who put a brave face on their troubles
- Aspen for people who are anxious or afraid but don't know why
- Beech for people who are intolerant and critical of others
- Centaury for people who allow others to impose on them
- Cerato for people who doubt their own judgment
- Cherry Plum for uncontrolled, irrational thoughts and the fear of doing something awful
- Chestnut Bud for people who repeat mistakes and don't learn from experience
- Chicory for over-possessive, selfish people who cling to their loved ones
- Clematis for day-dreamers
- Crab Apple for those who dislike something about the way they look and as a general cleanser
- Elm for responsible, capable people who in a crisis doubt their ability to cope
- Gentian for people disheartened when something goes wrong
- Gorse for people who have lost hope, often without cause
- Heather for talkative types who are obsessed with their own problems
- Holly for negative feelings of hatred, envy, jealousy and suspicion
- Honeysuckle for people who live in the past
- Hornbeam for mental tiredness at the thought of a coming task
- Impatiens for impatience and irritation at other people's slowness
- Larch for fear of failure and lack of confidence
- Mimulus for people who are afraid of something real that they can name

- Mustard for gloom and depression with no known cause
- Oak for strong, indefatigable people who can over-extend themselves by trying too hard
- Olive for people physically drained by exertion or illness
- Pine for those who blame themselves when things go wrong
- Red Chestnut for excessive worry about the welfare of loved ones
- Rock Rose for extreme fright and terror
- Rock Water for people whose self-discipline and high standards are carried to excess
- Scleranthus for people who find it hard to choose between possible courses of action
- Star of Bethlehem for sudden frights and shock
- Sweet Chestnut for utter despair and anguish
- Vervain for enthusiastic people who are always on the go
- Vine for domineering people
- Walnut to help protect against outside influences and the effects of change
- Water Violet for private, reserved people who can appear proud and arrogant
- White Chestnut for persistent worrying thoughts
- Wild Oat for people unable to find a direction for their lives
- Wild Rose for people who resign themselves without complaint or effort to everything life throws at them
- Willow for people who are full of self-pity, resentment and bitterness.

When using the Bach Flower Remedies it is essential to ignore as far as possible any physical symptoms or disease. This can be hard to do, but the physical side of disease can of course be treated using any other appropriate system of healing, whether orthodox or complementary. The Bach Flower Remedies themselves are selected according to the personality of the person being treated. For example, a kind gentle person who found it hard to say 'no' to other people would be given Centaury, while someone who always tries to laugh things off even when he is undergoing torture inside would

need Agrimony. In addition, the current mental state is taken into account so that someone who was worrying all the time would need White Chestnut while someone who was feeling a bit despondent after a setback would be given Gentian.

The effect of the remedies is to transform negative thoughts and behaviour into positive ones. They do not of course alter the personality or bring instant nirvana or bring back your past lives – instead they bring you gently back to yourself so that you can go on learning from the life that you are living now. So taking Centaury would not turn a kind person into a bossy tyrant; she would still be gentle and kind; but in addition she would be better able to draw the line and as a result wouldn't suffer from exploitation by more ruthless characters. And the White Chestnut worrier would be able to think more constructively about problems instead of circling endlessly around them and never reaching a rational conclusion.

Dr Bach once gave nine remedies to one of his patients at a single time, but in practice it is possible in almost all cases to limit the number given to six or seven. There are two main ways to take them. One is to put two drops of each selected remedy into a glass of water and sip from this at least four times a day – more if necessary – or until the problem has passed. Alternatively the two drops can be put into a clean empty 30ml dropper bottle which is then topped up with mineral water. From this bottle – known as a treatment bottle – four drops are taken four times a day. Kept in the fridge and used regularly a treatment bottle will last up to three weeks.

The treatment bottle dose is the minimum needed for the remedies to work effectively. You can take them more frequently for moments of crisis, because they are completely safe: it is impossible to overdose on them or become addicted or build up tolerance. In addition the Bach Flower Remedies do not affect the actions of other medicines or therapies, nor are they affected by them. This and the fact that they are free of side-effects makes them an ideal complement to other courses of treatment. You should always keep in mind, however, that the remedies are preserved in neat brandy, and for this reason use caution when giving them to recovering alcoholics or people who are allergic to alcohol or object to its use on religious or moral grounds.

As for the Rescue Remedy, it is a mix of five remedies – Rock Rose for terror, Clematis for light-headedness, Impatiens for agitation, Cherry Plum for loss of self-control and Star of Bethlehem for shock. Dr Bach selected these five remedies because he felt there would be at least something in the mix that would help anyone going through a crisis. To take it you simply put four drops in a glass of water and sip as required – and in an emergency, if there is no water available, you can put the drops straight on the tongue or rub them on the pulse points. Common uses for Rescue Remedy include calming down the victims of accidents and combating pre-operation nerves. Many midwives use them to help mothers through labour.

Dr Bach's remedies are still made today at the Bach Centre, Mount Vernon, the cottage in England where he spent the last years of his life. Since 1991 practitioner courses have been run at the Centre and are now run in the USA, Canada, Spain, Holland and Ireland as well. As a result more than 350 trained practitioners are now registered with the Centre.

• For more information contact The Dr Edward Bach Centre, Mount Vernon, Bakers Lane, Sotwell, Oxon OX10 0PZ, England. Or visit the web site at www.bachcentre.com

Questioning the alternative

Scientific assessment of complementary and alternative therapies

Interest in complementary and alternative medicine (CAM) is growing rapidly, driven principally by increased public demand. In the UK, it is estimated that 20 per cent of the population use these therapies, spending over £500 million a year. In the USA the proportion is even higher: 40 per cent of the population regularly use CAM, spending £15-20 billion a year between them. There are now more CAM practitioners than GPs in the UK, and some treatments are even delivered on the NHS. With this level of popularity, the CAM phenomenon cannot be ignored by the Western medical establishment.

On 10 March 2000 an all-day workshop at the Wellcome Trust brought together researchers and practitioners from a wide range of different fields in CAM and orthodox medicine. The aim was to discuss research issues in CAM and help inform Trust policy making in this area.

Why have such therapies become so popular? One reason is that CAM, like counselling services, has developed in response to certain needs that are not being met by modern medicine: in particular, there is evidence that people turn to CAM for complex, relapsing, possibly stress-related conditions, such as chronic fatigue syndrome and allergies, that do not respond well to conventional treatment. CAM practitioners tend to take a 'holistic' view, looking at the patient as an individual rather than a set of symptoms, an approach at odds with the typically more reductionist interventions of conventional medicine.

The strong emphasis placed on the patient-practitioner relationship is also important, a stark contrast to the NHS, where the time doctors can devote to their patients is frequently eroded (the average duration of an NHS consultation is 4.6 minutes). In addition, alternative medicine is empowering, since products can be bought over the counter without recourse to doctors' prescriptions. Nevertheless, in general, patients want to augment rather than replace the care they are getting from their doctors, and most CAM consultations take place in parallel with orthodox medicine.

> **At present CAM products are not classified as medicines, and there may be a need to standardise and even license products before they are offered to the public**

Unfortunately, the very elements that appeal to the patient pose difficulties for rigorous scientific assessment of CAM. Therapies are often aimed at improving general well-being – an outcome that is vague and hard to measure. Moreover, a vast spectrum of diverse remedies fall under the general umbrella of CAM therapies. Although some of these, such as herbal medicine, have agents that can be isolated and tested (artemisinin, derived from the ancient Chinese herbal remedy quinghaosu, is now an important treatment for malaria), some, like crystal therapy, appear to have no plausible mechanism of action. To cloud matters further, CAM tends to use cultural explanations or indeterminate terms such as 'readjust balances' or 'restore homeostasis' rather than precise, scientific terminology.

There has also been little definition of what exactly people expect from these therapies – whether they are intended to cure or contain disease, for example – and this lack of clarity extends to the use of CAM in NHS primary care. GPs often refer patients to CAM practitioners for general reasons,

because the patient is distressed, rather than because of any specific condition. On the other hand, despite what science might call this 'vagueness', the psychological 'feel good' factor integral to so many CAM therapies may in itself have a significant effect in terms of clinical improvement. Indeed, the 'placebo effect' – the medicine improvement shown by patients treated with an inert or dummy treatment in medical trials – is further evidence of the potential importance of psychological factors.

Nevertheless, despite these difficulties, CAM therapies should be amenable to rigorous scientific enquiry. A sophisticated level of thinking will be required to develop methodology to look at psychological, physiological and nutritional variables simultaneously – but it should still be achievable. Randomised controlled trials could be adapted to answer more than one question at a time, and large-scale observational studies and sophisticated statistical analysis would also be as useful in the assessment of CAM as in conventional medicine.

Trial design may therefore be difficult but not impossible. However, the difficulties in scientifically assessing CAM are compounded by the absence of a research base able to carry out the experiments. Not only does CAM lack specialist centres and library resources, it also has no real evaluative tradition or culture, and much of the evidence to date is anecdotal, heterogeneous and fragmented. Studies have been conducted either without placebo controls, making them unreliable by today's rigorous standards of evidence-based medicine, or with small samples in restricted populations from which it is difficult to generalise results.

Despite a general perception that funding bodies are biased against their field, funding is available for good-quality applications in the UK. Both the Wellcome Trust and the Medical Research Council will fund CAM proposals if the science is of a high enough standard. The success rate for CAM applications to the Trust is actually higher than for

'conventional' research proposals. Nevertheless, the number of applications received is very small.

In the USA, the situation is rather different. The National Center for Complementary and Alternative Medicine (NCCAM) was established in 1998 specifically to support CAM research; NCCAM will spend $68.7 million this year. This 'ring-fencing' of money for CAM through NCCAM is a powerful way of encouraging research. It attracts high-quality researchers, inspires CAM practitioners to join a research team, and helps overcome misconceptions that review panels are prejudiced against CAM. On the other hand, ring-fencing shields researchers from the competitive pressures of peer review and may mean poor-quality projects are funded. One compromise is for funds to be provided for a limited period to kick-start research, then phased out when the discipline is strong enough to compete with orthodox medical research.

The public sector clearly has an important role to play in safeguarding public health and assessing safety and effectiveness. But what of commercial bodies? Pharmaceutical companies routinely plough around 25 per cent of their profits back into research to evaluate the safety and efficacy of their agents before they appear on the market. Perhaps CAM manufacturers should be encouraged to do the same, for example by forming partnerships with funding bodies. At present CAM products are not classified as medicines, and there may be a need to standardise and even license products before they are offered to the public.

Another obstacle to research in CAM is the mutual suspicion that exists between the orthodox and alternative communities. Many scientists argue that money for CAM research is wasted on fantasy, whilst CAM practitioners often fear that truly valuable traditions will be undone by the demands of orthodox research – a cultural divide that clearly needs to be bridged if CAM research is to benefit from the mutual expertise in both fields. One solution might be to provide CAM practitioners with training in conventional research methodology, or to establish career development fellowships to attract high-calibre research scientists from the orthodox field into CAM research.

What are the possible ways forward for scientific investigation of CAM? A first step for the CAM community might be to set priorities, deciding which areas research should be focused on first. The placebo response is likely to be high on the lists. In fact, in November, NCCAM will lead an NIH-wide workshop on this effort in the USA, and issue a call for research proposals on the placebo response for next year. In Europe and the UK, there appears to be a need for some form of over-arching structure to co-ordinate disparate activities and help devise a coherent strategy for the development of research and education in CAM.

All this will require a considerable degree of collaboration and resources of time and money. Although there is enthusiasm in many quarters, a question mark remains over whether CAM research is actually going to move forwards in this country the way it has done in the USA under the auspices of the NIH and NCCAM.

The Wellcome Trust is actively considering the issue of CAM research but currently has no plans to launch a special initiative. A report on the Trust's workshop was presented to the House of Lords select committee on 23 May 2000.

• The above information is an extract from *Wellcome News*, the magazine produced by The Wellcome Trust.
© *The Wellcome Trust*

A little drop of flower power

Would essence of pansy and pear blossom, chosen by a crystal under the guidance of a therapist, help Verity Owen feel good?

Flower therapy is not as well known as, say, homoeopathy, but that may soon change. More and more people are turning to flower essences to treat emotional problems. The most popular range, created at the beginning of the 20th century by Dr Edward Bach, is available at high street chemists. But do they work? In need of a boost, I booked an appointment with Britain's leading flower therapist, Clare Harvey, whose clients include Lulu and the actress Janet McTeer.

The first thing that struck me when I arrived at the Hale Clinic, where Harvey practises in London, was how she looked. Her glamorous appearance could not have been further from the unusual-looking new age guru I'd been expecting. Harvey was brought up using the essences of Dr Bach, who is probably the most important figure in the development of flower therapies in Britain.

'My grandmother knew Edward Bach and learnt a great deal from him,' she says. 'She was also a healer, and she passed on everything she knew to me.' Harvey's desk was strewn with hundreds of bottles of flower essences. 'I've got essences from Australia, the Himalayas, from all over the world, in fact.'

After a brief health résumé, she began the diagnosis. She produced a small crystal on a silver thread and I began to panic. Would there be magic wands, too? Fortunately not.

Many flower therapists use the technique of 'dowsing', and Harvey assured me that this was the most effective way of prescribing remedies. She asked me to touch each of the bottles with my index finger, while she dangled a rose quartz crystal above my finger, allowing it to swing in a tight clockwise circle. Apparently, dowsing enables the patient to guide the practitioner to the right bottle.

Nothing happened at first – the crystal didn't crack or fly out of her hand as I had secretly hoped. But then, as we started going through the Australian Bush Essences, the crystal moved quite suddenly in an anti-clockwise direction. 'Aha,' she said, 'you've picked Black Eyed Susan. I thought you might pick that one: it's for people who are worn out and find it hard to slow down.'

> *More and more people are turning to flower essences to treat emotional problems*

Then she picked out another bottle. 'Pansy! This will help you cope with grief and it's good for your kidneys,' she said. (I was impressed. I suffer from repeated kidney infections and have been bereaved, although not recently.)

Some of the flower essences had familiar names such as Pear Blossom; others, such as Sky Blue Orchid and Jacaranda, were more exotic. Harvey seemed pleased with the choices I had made, all 13 of them. She prepared my concoction using a couple of drops of each essence, mineral water and brandy to act as a preservative. Finally, she used the dowsing technique to determine the dosage I needed – seven drops morning and night for two months.

Harvey told me not to expect immediate results, as the flowers are thought to work gently, and can take many weeks, if not months, to work. I left the clinic with my flower potions, and hurried home to look up the contents of my mixture in Harvey's flower essence encyclopaedia. It confirmed my suspicions: I was neurotic, anxious, directionless, needy and worn out. Surely it would take more than a few drops of pansy and pear blossom to sort that out? Still, I was willing to give it a go.

It is now two months since I started taking the flower essences. I haven't noticed any changes in my health, but I do seem to dream more. I can't decide whether I feel more

centred or focused. I did, however, enjoy the discipline of taking my flower blend twice a day, although I seem to have developed a rather worrying taste for brandy.

• Clare Harvey practises at the Hale Clinic in London (tel: 020 7631 0156) and at Middle Piccadilly Natural Healing Centre in Dorset (tel: 01963 23468; or look at the web site, www.middlepiccadilly.com). A one-hour consultation at the Hale Clinic costs £45.

The expert's view: it's all in the mind

By Professor Edzard Ernst

Dr Edward Bach was an unusual doctor. He claimed that the root of all illness was emotional imbalance: treat people's emotions and they become well.

Having qualified in 1912, he worked at the Royal London Homoeopathic Hospital as a microbiologist, before leaving London to spend several years in Wales, where he explored the countryside. He developed his theory that negative moods caused illness and began to believe that the only true healing agents were to be found in plants. Over several years, he identified 38 plant-based healing remedies to correspond with 38 negative emotional states. This was his system, just one of several varieties now available today.

Flower remedies are made by placing freshly picked flowers in a bowl of spring water left in the sun for several hours. This process is believed to 'energise' the water. Subsequently, the flower essence is preserved by adding brandy. The mechanism of action of these remedies remains unknown.

Proponents claim that flower remedies adjust imbalances within the patient's emotional perceptions. Sceptics argue that the remedies contain nothing but water and brandy, and that any therapeutic response must be due to a placebo effect.

Who is right? Anecdotal reports suggest that Bach remedies may be effective in treating a huge range of conditions, including addiction, amnesia, bites and stings, bunions, infertility, insomnia, psoriasis, panic attacks and sexual dysfunction.

Flower remedies are not marketed as medicines, so there is no obligation for manufacturers to back up claims with evidence. At the University of Exeter, we tested the effects of the 'five flower remedy' on stress, the condition it is marketed for. This mixture, also sold as 'rescue remedy', is the most widely used of all flower remedies. It is composed of clematis, impatiens, rock rose, cherry plum and star of Bethlehem. We recruited 100 students who took either the real thing or placebos to alleviate their 'exam nerves'. We made sure that the real treatment was indistinguishable from the placebo. In technical terms, our study was a randomised, double-blind, placebo-controlled trial, which simply means it was the most rigorous clinical test possible.

Our results show no differences between the 'five flower remedy' and the placebo. Unfortunately, some students proved to be unreliable and we could only evaluate 45 of them.

Sceptics argue that the remedies contain nothing but water and brandy, and that any therapeutic response must be due to a placebo effect

---

Yet the results are conclusive: 'five flower remedy' is not an effective treatment for examination stress.

Unknown to us, scientists from the University of Freiburg in Germany carried out a study that was similar. They recruited 61 students suffering from exam stress and treated them with 'rescue remedy' or with placebo. Their results show that students in both groups responded positively, but there was no difference between the placebo and the real thing. Our German colleagues conclude that 'flower remedies are an effective placebo for test anxiety which do not have a specific effect'.

This highlights the power of the placebo. Dummy pills can alleviate pain and reduce examination stress. Some would say that charging considerable amounts of money to sell placebos constitutes harm, but placebos can be helpful, although lay literature often misleads the public into unrealistic expectations.

Individuals might be induced to try remedies for seemingly innocent symptoms, and might initially believe them successful. Only too late will they consult a doctor who may then diagnose a serious disease that would have been curable had they only visited earlier.

• Edzard Ernst is director of the Department of Complementary Medicine at the University of Exeter

Alternative medicine

Information from the Christian Medical Fellowship (CMF)

By Peter Saunders

Alternative medicine is rising rapidly up the healthcare agenda. One in four people in the UK use at least one form of alternative medicine and three out of four people are in favour of alternative therapies being available on the NHS.

One study cited by a recent BMA report suggested that there may be up to 15 million consultations to non-conventional therapists each year in the UK, with about 1.5 million people (2.5% of the population) each year receiving treatment.

The British Register of Complementary Practitioners has 1,000 members and the number is rising by 10% per year. A 1980 UK survey suggested that there were 12.1 non-medically qualified practitioners per 100,000 population – 27% of the number of general practitioners. In addition, 35% of UK GPs have received some training in alternative medicine.

In most member states of the European Union (e.g. Belgium, France, Spain, Italy and Greece) the practice of medicine by non-recognised health professionals is illegal. In Germany and Scandinavia there is some regulation but in the United Kingdom and Ireland there is virtually no regulation at all.

When one considers the tight controls on the training and practice of orthodox medical practitioners there is clearly a double standard operating. If there are no proper controls for alternative medicine practitioners, then the way is open for charlatans, profiteers and tricksters to operate alongside those who are genuinely providing service of proven value.

What is alternative medicine?
Problems of definition
The report of the BMA's Board of Science and Education's working party, *Complementary Medicine, New Approaches to Good Practice* defines non-conventional therapies as 'those which are not widely used by orthodox medical professionals nor widely taught at undergraduate level in medical and paramedical courses' – but some therapies regarded as alternative in the UK are taught formally in medical schools elsewhere.

The three terms complementary, alternative and holistic are used almost interchangeably – but convey different messages. 'Alternative' implies an either/or relationship with orthodox medicine; 'complementary' a both/and relationship while 'holistic' implies that non-orthodox therapies treat the 'whole person'. All these assumptions are controversial.

The diversity of therapies
The BMA report says that as many as 160 different forms of non-conventional therapy have been identified. An A to Z of some of the most common includes:

Acupuncture, Acupressure, Alexander Technique, Aromatherapy, Auricular Therapy, Bach Flower Remedies, Chiropractic, Crystal Therapy, Herbs, Homeopathy, Hypnosis, Iridology, Macrobiotics, Massage, Naturopathy, Osteopathy, Reflexology, Shiatsu, Therapeutic Touch, Transcendental Meditation (TM), Yoga, Zen and Zone Therapy.

On first glance there seems to be very little similarity between one form of alternative medicine and another; but what unifies most of them is the idea of a 'life force' or 'vital energy' which ensures health, becomes disrupted in disease and can be manipulated by various means.

For example, underlying acupuncture is the belief that there is a vital force or energy called 'Chi' which flows freely through the body in twelve meridians or channels. The flow of this energy depends on the balance between two opposite forces; an active, 'male' force called 'yin' and a passive, 'female' force called 'yang'. When the flow of the Chi energy is free and uninterrupted health is ensured but if the balance between yin and yang is disturbed or if there is any blockage to energy flow then disease results.

These ideas have their roots in the ancient Chinese religion of Taoism which has Chi, yin and yang as fundamental concepts.

Ideologies which underlie other forms of medicine use different words for the same general concept of 'life force'. Shiatsu is based on Shintoism and calls the energy 'Ki'. Yoga and TM are based on Hinduism and call the force 'prana'. Homeopathy uses the term 'vital energy', chiropractic 'innate intelligence' and Maori medicine terms the life force 'mana'.

The common theme of 'correcting imbalance'
In most alternative therapies health is believed to be restored by relieving blockage and restoring flow in the

'life force', but the means whereby this is achieved vary widely as listed below:

Method	Modality
Acupuncture	Needling
Homeopathy	Minute doses of diluted medicine
Reflexology	Foot massage
Aromatherapy	Aromatic oils
Yoga	Adopting body postures
Transcendental Meditation	Meditation
Therapeutic Touch	Hovering hands
Macrobiotics	Diet

Why is alternative medicine so popular?

There are seven main factors accounting for the rise in popularity of alternative medicine in the Western world.

1. Changes in the Western world-view

Two hundred years ago in Britain most people had a Christian world-view; they believed in a creator God who made us, who intervened in our world and to whom we were accountable. But with the publication of Darwin's *Origin of the Species* and the rise of biblical criticism, this theistic world view gave way to an atheistic one.

People began to doubt the existence of God and life after death. Man came to be seen simply as a clever monkey, the product of matter, chance and time in a directionless and purposeless universe. Morality became relative ('what's right for me') rather than absolute.

Now we are seeing another world-view shift from atheism into pantheism. Pantheism is the ideology which lies behind Eastern religions like Hinduism and also the New Age Movement. God is an impersonal force of which we are all simply a part. Death leads to reincarnation, and morality simply means being in harmony with nature. All is one and all is God. This has meant an increasing openness to all sorts of non-Christian spiritual belief along with a scepticism and suspicion about science.

The change of world-view from theism, to atheism and then pantheism has had profound effects on the way that medicine is practised.

While Christian doctors see human beings as a tri-unity of spirit, soul (or mind) and body (1 Thess 5:23), atheistic doctors see them as consisting of just body and mind. By contrast, New Age or alternative medicine practitioners see human beings as an integrated whole; but from a pantheistic rather than a theistic perspective.

Much of alternative medicine has its roots in the New Age Movement which in turn is rooted in astrology. Exponents believe that for the last 2,000 years we have been in the age of Pisces (the fishes), but that now we are moving into the age of Aquarius (the water-carrier). The age of Pisces was characterised by rationality, logic, objectivity and black and white analytical 'left brain' thinking. By contrast the age of Aquarius is characterised by intuitional, subjective, grey 'right brain' thinking.

Sociologically the New Age Movement spawned the counterculture of the 1960s with 'flower-power', peace protests, drug experimentation and the Hippie movement. Spiritually it paved the way for a wide acceptance of Eastern religious ideology, astrology and the occult. Medically the New Age Movement has meant an increasing disillusionment with and scepticism about scientific medicine.

As Christians we reject both the atheistic and pantheistic world-views. They are quite simply not the way the world is. God does exist. We are made in his image, yet fallen; and death leads to judgement. We embrace the scientific method as a gift of God, but we also see human beings as being more than simply the sum of their parts.

2. Failings of orthodox medicine

There have been great advances in orthodox medicine over the last two centuries which have led to the eradication and alleviation of many diseases which were previously neither preventable nor curable: immunisations for smallpox, antibiotics for infection, anti-psychotics for schizophrenia, chemotherapy for cancer, drugs for heart failure and surgery for a whole host of structural and anatomical problems.

But medicine also has its limits. With many illnesses we have a long way to go. Solid tumours (e.g. lung, breast and bowel) are in general difficult to treat if surgery fails. There is still much progress to be made in chronic diseases like multiple sclerosis and rheumatoid arthritis, and there is still no orthodox cure for musculoskeletal back pain and the common cold. If we also consider that 75% of people seeing their doctor do not have any defined organic illness, it is easy to see why people may decide to consult alternative practitioners. Patients may also become impatient or disillusioned with the NHS system of referrals and waiting lists.

With some diseases alternative medicine fares no worse than orthodox medicine and it is in these areas that alternative medicine thrives.

3. Medical arrogance

Doctors have not always been ready to admit failure; and on occasions may go on using treatments of doubtful value, or with potential side-effects rather than being honest that nothing else can be done. The inappropriate use of some chemotherapeutic agents or radical surgery for advanced cancer, for instance, may cultivate distrust in patients who then seek other solutions.

4. The side-effects of orthodox medicine

Orthodox medicines and surgery can produce side-effects and complications which are sometimes fatal. Examples are often widely publicised by an unforgiving press. By contrast most alternative medicine has little in the way of side-effects.

5. Loss of a whole-person perspective

Advances in the science of medicine may be at the expense of the art of medicine. Doctors have less time for the patient, touch patients less often, and are tempted much more now to treat their patients simply as anatomical structures or biochemical machines. There is much less in medicine now of the ritual handshake, pulse-taking, hand on the shoulder etc. Too often the doctor is now esconced behind his PC and perhaps a formidable desk; while many alternative therapies involve plenty of 'hands-on' diagnosis and treatment.

Alternative medical practitioners generally are able to give much more in terms of time and touch, thereby engendering more trust. Homeopaths, for example, may spend up to 90 minutes in a first consultation and 45 minutes on follow-up. Patients naturally assume, 'He must know what he is doing because he spends so much time with me.'

6. Costs of high-tech medicine
High-tech medicine is expensive, while often the only cost of alternative medicine is the therapist's time. This is one feature making alternative therapies increasingly attractive to NHS managers looking to cut costs.

7. Consumer demand
Patients are prepared to pay for therapies which promise what orthodox medicine has failed to deliver; especially for incurable cancer or chronic pain. This demand means that there is plenty of room in the market place for more practitioners.

Why does alternative medicine seem to work?

Why is it that so many people are seeking alternative medicine therapies when so many of them have been shown not to work in clinical trials? There are at least eight reasons why.

1. Genuine therapeutic effects
Some alternative medicines genuinely work. Over half of prescription and over-the-counter drugs originate as natural compounds or are based on them (e.g. aspirin, digitalis, morphine, adrenaline, curare, all antibiotics except the quinolones etc.); and the natural world may hold many more therapeutic treasures.

It is quite conceivable that some alternative medicine practitioners are using useful compounds or techniques which are not yet known to orthodox medicine. But if this is the case then we need to discover what they are so that they can be isolated and given in the correct dose!

2. The placebo effect
If we strongly believe that something

(or someone) has the power to help us, then we are much more likely to experience benefit. It is a fact that one-third of people given an inert compound to relieve a particular symptom will report relief of that symptom. This is called the placebo effect. In the same way patients who share the therapist's belief in New Age pantheism or the existence of 'life force' will be more likely to benefit from their therapy.

3. Concurrent use of therapies
Belief in an alternative therapy's effectiveness may develop when it is used concurrently with another more effective orthodox therapy. The effect is then wrongly ascribed to the alternative therapy.

4. Psychosomatic illness
Many illnesses are psychosomatic; in other words a patient's stress level or mental state can aggravate the symptoms. Asthma, eczema, peptic ulcer and rheumatoid arthritis fall in this category. Alternative therapies which induce relaxation may then improve the symptoms.

5. Spontaneous remissions
Many diseases get better by themselves. Viral infections (e.g. warts, common cold) and some tumours (e.g. malignant melanoma) are examples of conditions which may spontaneously regress. In such cases people may well then attribute therapeutic effect to the remedy they were trying at the time of recovery, when in fact their improvement at that time may just have been coincidence. This is called the 'post hoc, propter hoc' fallacy; in other words 'because B followed A, then A must have caused B'.

6. Dietary influences
There is a strong link between diet and health, and many alternative therapists recommend that patients drink less coffee or alcohol, eat less fat or more fibre or take vitamins. The resulting improvement may then be due to the change in diet, rather than the alternative therapy being used concurrently.

7. Imagined improvement
Some patients, especially if open to suggestion from others that they 'look better', may simply imagine that they

'feel better'; especially if the symptoms were of a vague nature in the first place. Alternatively they may simply get better at tolerating symptoms, and imagine that the symptoms themselves have diminished.

8. Demonic involvement
There may be real spiritual forces operating to bring healing through demonic power. Such healings may be the bait that Satan then uses to draw a person more deeply into the occult, or into accepting a pantheistic world-view.

Summary
We have reviewed the rapid rise in popularity in alternative medicine, and seen that while therapies are diverse, there is a pantheistic ideology behind many of them.

Alternative medicine is popular because of changes in the Western world-view, the perceived failings, arrogance, costs and side-effects of orthodox medicine, and because it appears to bring a 'whole-person' perspective.

While some therapies may genuinely work, apparent improvements are often due to other reasons such as spontaneous remissions, the use of concurrent orthodox medicine or the placebo effect.

Each branch of alternative medicine needs to be assessed individually to determine its effectiveness, scientific basis, mode of action, safety, underlying world-view and links with the occult.

We should be wary, but we must be careful also that we do not miss genuine gifts which God has given. The biblical injunction to 'test everything . . . hold on to the good . . . avoid every kind of evil' (1 Thess 5:21,22) is surely as relevant here as in any other area of the Christian life.

● This is an abridged version of a CMF article in which Peter Saunders gives an overview of the field and suggests some principles to apply in assessing individual modalities. The full version can be found on the CMF web site at www.cmf.org.uk/pubs/nucleus/nucapr99/altern.htm

What is complementary medicine?

Definitions and terms

Complementary medicine refers to a group of therapeutic and diagnostic disciplines that exist largely outside the institutions where conventional health care is taught and provided. Complementary medicine is an increasing feature of healthcare practice, but considerable confusion remains about what exactly it is and what position the disciplines included under this term should hold in relation to conventional medicine.

In the 1970s and 1980s these disciplines were mainly provided as an alternative to conventional health care and hence became known collectively as 'alternative medicine'. The name 'complementary medicine' developed as the two systems began to be used alongside (to 'complement') each other. Over the years, 'complementary' has changed from describing this relation between unconventional healthcare disciplines and conventional care to defining the group of disciplines itself. Some authorities use the term 'unconventional medicine' synonymously. This changing and overlapping terminology may explain some of the confusion that surrounds the subject.

Common complementary therapies

- Acupressure
- Acupuncture
- Alexander technique
- Applied kinesiology
- Anthroposophic medicine
- Aromatherapy
- Autogenic training
- Ayurveda
- Chiropractic
- Cranial osteopathy
- Environmental medicine
- Healing
- Herbal medicine
- Homoeopathy
- Hypnosis
- Massage
- Meditation

By Catherine Zollman and Andrew Vickers

- Naturopathy
- Nutritional therapy
- Osteopathy
- Reflexology
- Reiki
- Relaxation and visualisation
- Shiatsu
- Therapeutic touch
- Yoga

Definition of complementary medicine adopted by Cochrane Collaboration

'Complementary and alternative medicine (CAM) is a broad domain of healing resources that encompasses all health systems, modalities, and practices and their accompanying theories and beliefs, other than those intrinsic to the politically dominant health system of a particular society or culture in a given historical period. CAM includes all such practices and ideas self-defined by their users as preventing or treating illness or promoting health and well-being. Boundaries within CAM and between the CAM domain and that of the dominant system are not always sharp or fixed.'

We use the term complementary medicine to describe healthcare practices such as those listed above. We use it synonymously with the terms 'complementary therapies' and 'complementary and alternative medicine' found in other texts, according to the definition used by the Cochrane Collaboration.

Which disciplines are complementary?

Our list is not exhaustive, and new branches of established disciplines are continually being developed. Also, what is thought to be conventional varies between countries and changes over time. The boundary between complementary and conventional medicine is therefore blurred and constantly shifting. For example, although osteopathy and chiropractic are still generally considered complementary therapies in Britain, they are included as part of standard care in guidelines from conventional bodies such as the Royal College of General Practitioners.

Unhelpful assumptions about complementary medicine

'Non-statutory – not provided by the NHS'
- Complementary medicine is increasingly available on the NHS
- 39% of general practitioners provide access to complementary medicine for NHS patients

'Unregulated – therapists not regulated by state legislation'
- Osteopaths and chiropractors are now state registered and regulated, and other disciplines will probably soon follow
- Substantial amount of complementary medicine is delivered by conventional health professionals

'Unconventional – not taught in medical schools'
- Disciplines such as physiotherapy and chiropody are also not taught in medical schools
- Some medical schools have a complementary medicine component as part of the curriculum

'Natural'
- Good conventional medicine also involves rehabilitation with, say, rest, exercise, or diet
- Complementary medicine may involve unnatural practices such as injecting mistletoe or inserting needles into the skin

'Holistic – treats the whole person'
- Many conventional healthcare professionals work in a holistic manner
- Complementary therapists can be narrow and reductionist in their approach
- Holism relates more to outlook of practitioner than to the type of medicine practised

'Alternative'
- Implies use instead of conventional treatment
- Most users of complementary medicine seem not to have abandoned conventional medicine

'Unproved'
- There is a growing body of evidence that certain complementary therapies are effective in certain clinical conditions

- Many conventional healthcare practices are not supported by the results of controlled clinical trials

'Irrational – no scientific basis'
- Scientific research is starting to uncover the mechanisms of some complementary therapies, such as acupuncture and hypnosis

'Harmless'
- There are reports of serious adverse effects associated with using complementary medicine

The wide range of disciplines classified as complementary medicine makes it difficult to find defining criteria that are common to all. Many of the assumptions made about complementary medicine are oversimplistic generalisations.

Organisational structure

Historical development
Since the inception of the NHS, the public sector has supported training, regulation, research, and practice in conventional health care. The recent development of complementary medicine has taken place largely in the private sector. Until recently, most complementary practitioners trained in small, privately funded colleges and then worked independently in relative isolation from other practitioners.

Factors limiting research in complementary medicine

Lack of funding
In 1995 only 0.08% of NHS research funds were spent on complementary medicine. Many funding bodies have been reluctant to give grants for research in complementary medicine. Pharmaceutical companies

have little commercial interest in researching complementary medicine

Lack of research skills
Complementary practitioners usually have no training in critical evaluation of existing research or practical research skills

Lack of an academic infrastructure
This means limited access to computer and library facilities, statistical support, academic supervision, and university research grants

Insufficient patient numbers
Individual list sizes are small, and most practitioners have no disease 'specialty' and therefore see very small numbers of patients with the same clinical condition. Recruiting patients into studies is difficult in private practice

Difficulty undertaking and interpreting systematic reviews
Many poor quality studies make interpretation of results difficult. Many publications in complementary medicine are not on standard databases such as Medline. Many different types of treatment exist within each complementary discipline (for example, formula, individualised, electro, laser, and auricular acupuncture)

Methodological issues
Responses to treatment are unpredictable and individual, and treatment is usually not standardised. Designing appropriate controls for some complementary therapies (such as acupuncture, manipulation) is difficult, as is blinding patients to treatment allocation. Allowing for the role of the therapeutic relationship also creates problems

Research
More complementary medical research exists than is commonly recognised – the Cochrane Library lists over 4000 randomised trials – but the field is still poorly researched compared with conventional medicine. There are several reasons for this, some of which also apply to conventional disciplines like occupational and speech therapy. However, complementary practitioners are

increasingly aware of the value of research, and many complementary training courses now include research skills. Conventional sources of funding, such as the NHS research and development programme and major cancer charities, have become more open to complementary researchers.

Training

Although complementary practitioners (other than osteopaths and chiropractors) can legally practise without any training whatsoever, most have completed some further education in their chosen discipline.

There is great variation in the many training institutions. For the major therapies – osteopathy, chiropractic, acupuncture, herbal medicine, and homoeopathy – these tend to be highly developed, some with university affiliation, degree-level exams, and external assessment. Others, particularly those teaching less invasive therapies such as reflexology and aromatherapy, tend to be small and isolated, determine curricula internally, and have idiosyncratic assessment procedures. In some courses direct clinical contact is limited. Some are not recognised by the main registering bodies in the relevant discipline. Most complementary practitioners finance their training without state support, and many train part time over several years.

Conventional healthcare practitioners such as nurses and doctors often have their own separate training courses in complementary medicine.

Regulation

Apart from osteopaths and chiropractors, complementary practitioners are not obliged to join any official register before setting up in practice. However, many practitioners are now members of appropriate registering or accrediting bodies. There are between 150 and 300 such organisations, with varying membership size and professional standards. Some complementary disciplines have as many as 50 registering organisations, all with different criteria and standards.

Recognising that this situation

is unsatisfactory, many disciplines are taking steps to become unified under one regulatory body per discipline. Such bodies should, as a minimum, have published criteria for entry, established codes of conduct, complaints procedures, and disciplinary sanctions and should require members to be fully insured.

The General Osteopathic Council and General Chiropractic Council have been established by acts of parliament and have statutory self-regulatory status and similar powers and functions to those of the General Medical Council. A small number of other disciplines – such as acupuncture, herbal medicine, and homoeopathy – have a single main regulatory body and are working towards statutory self-regulation.

Efficient regulation of the 'less invasive' complementary therapies such as massage or relaxation therapies is equally important. However, statutory regulation, with its requirements for parliamentary legislation and expensive bureaucratic procedures, may not be feasible. Legal and ethics experts argue that unified and efficient voluntary self-regulatory bodies that fulfil the minimum standards listed above should be sufficient to safeguard patients. It will be some years before even this is achieved across the board.

Approaches to treatment

The approaches used by different complementary practitioners have some common features. Although they are not shared by all complementary disciplines, and some apply to conventional disciplines as

well, understanding them may help to make sense of patients' experiences of complementary medicine.

The holistic approach

Many, but not all, complementary practitioners have a multifactorial and multilevel view of human illness. Disease is thought to result from disturbances at a combination of physical, psychological, social, and spiritual levels. The body's capacity for self-repair, given appropriate conditions, is emphasised.

Example of a holistic approach – Rudolph Steiner's central tenets of anthroposophy

- Each individual is unique
- Scientific, artistic, and spiritual insights may need to be applied together to restore health
- Life has meaning and purpose – the loss of this sense may lead to a deterioration in health
- Illness may provide opportunities for positive change and a new balance in our lives

According to most complementary practitioners, the purpose of therapeutic intervention is to restore balance and facilitate the body's own healing responses rather than to target individual disease processes or stop troublesome symptoms. They may therefore prescribe a package of care, which could include modification of lifestyle, dietary change, and exercise as well as a specific treatment. Thus, a medical herbalist may give counselling, an exercise regimen, guidance on breathing and relaxation, dietary advice, and a herbal prescription.

It should be stressed that this holistic approach is not unique to complementary practice. Good conventional general practice, for example, follows similar principles.

Use of unfamiliar terms and ideas

Complementary practitioners often use terms and ideas that are not easily translated into Western scientific language. For example, neither the reflex zones manipulated in reflexology nor the 'Qi energy' fundamental to traditional Chinese medicine have any known anatomical or physiological correlates.

Sometimes familiar terms are used but with a different meaning: acupuncturists may talk of 'taking the pulse', but they will be assessing characteristics such as 'wiriness' or 'slipperiness', which have no Western equivalent. It is important not to interpret terms used in complementary medicine too literally and to understand that they are sometimes used metaphorically or as a shorthand for signs, symptoms, and syndromes that are not recognised in conventional medicine.

Different categorisation of illness

Complementary and conventional practitioners often have very different methods of assessing and diagnosing patients. Thus, a patient's condition may be described as 'deficient liver Qi' by a traditional acupuncturist, a 'pulsatilla constitution' by a homoeopath, and 'a peptic ulcer' by a conventional doctor. In each case the way the problem is diagnosed determines the treatment given.

Confusingly, there is little correlation between the different diagnostic systems: some patients with deficient liver Qi do not have ulcers, and some ulcer patients do not have deficient liver Qi but another traditional Chinese diagnosis. This causes problems when comparing complementary and conventional treatments in defined patient groups.

It should be stressed that the lack of a shared world-view is not necessarily a barrier to effective co-operation. For example, doctors work closely alongside hospital chaplains and social workers, each regarding the others as valued members of the healthcare team.

Approaches to learning and teaching

Complementary practitioners are not generally concerned with understanding the basic scientific mechanism of their particular therapy. Their knowledge base is often derived from a tradition of clinical observation and treatment decisions are usually empirical. Sometimes traditional teachings are handed down in a way that discourages questioning and evolution of practice, or encourages reliance on their own and others' individual anecdotal clinical and intuitive experience.

Conclusion

It is obvious from this discussion that complementary medicine is a heterogeneous subject. It is unlikely that all complementary disciplines will have an equal impact on UK health practices.

• *The ABC of complementary medicine* is edited and written by Catherine Zollman and Andrew Vickers. Catherine Zollman is a general practitioner in Bristol, and Andrew Vickers will shortly take up a post at Memorial Sloan-Kettering Cancer Center, New York. At the time of writing, both worked for the Research Council for Complementary Medicine, London.

It works – up to a point

The power of acupuncture is probably greater than sceptics want to admit but weaker than enthusiasts realise, says Edzard Ernst

An anecdote from China, dating back to the 5th century, tells the story of the governor of the province of Luzhou and his painful shoulder. The problem particularly annoyed him because it interfered with his archery, and the celebrated physician Zhen Quan was summoned.

After examining the governor, the physician told him to face the target with his bow and arrow and take aim. As he did so, Zhen Quan stood behind him and thrust a needle in the acupuncture point on the tip of the shoulder. The response was dramatic and immediate: the arrow flew straight to the bull's-eye and the governor was cured of his pain.

The history of acupuncture is filled with colourful tales of this type – but anecdotes are no longer sufficient to persuade us of the effectiveness of therapeutic interventions. Today, we want evidence-based medicine.

Is there evidence that acupuncture works? The answer is yes. It is probably more effective than most sceptics want to admit, but it is also less so than many enthusiasts realise.

Traditional acupuncturists believe that our bodies are governed by a life energy flowing in channels called meridians. This energy is a balance of opposing characteristics, called yin and yang. Every illness is understood as the expression of an imbalance between yin and yang. One way of re-establishing the balance is to insert needles in acupuncture points located along the meridians.

Instead of needles, other means of stimulation can be used – such as pressure, laser light, electrical currents or heat. Neither the meridians nor the acupuncture points have been identified scientifically and, because the concept of yin and yang is more an ancient philosophy than a fact, critics have always insisted that no sound scientific rationale of acupuncture exists.

In the early 1970s, when President Nixon visited China, this situation began to change. One member of his entourage fell ill and required immediate surgery. His pain during and after the operation was controlled by acupuncture. Back home in America, he publicised his extraordinary experience widely and this sparked off a flurry of research.

As a consequence, we now have a reasonable understanding of how the treatment might work. The theory is that acupuncture activates certain areas in the brain thought to be involved in pain control, releasing transmitter substances that have powerful effects on pain perception.

Such lines of research opened up new ways of thinking about acupuncture and led to the emergence of 'Western' or 'scientific' acupuncture. There are considerable differences between traditional Chinese treatments and the Western variety. In the former, conventional diagnoses are not normally sought and treatment is usually tailored according to each patient's particular yin/yang imbalance.

Western acupuncturists do not personalise treatment to that extent, but direct it at the conventional diagnosis established beforehand. While traditional acupuncturists tend to view acupuncture as a 'cure-all', Western acupuncturists strive to discriminate between those ailments for which it is helpful and those for which there is little positive evidence.

Hundreds of clinical studies have been carried out to determine whether acupuncture works for certain conditions. Studies of this type are fraught with numerous problems.

What, for instance, is an acceptable 'placebo' (dummy treatment) for an intervention therapy such as acupuncture? It is hardly surprising that the findings are not uniform.

While it is tempting to pick out those trials that confirm one's beliefs, it is also obvious that this can be grossly misleading. The fairest way to evaluate acupuncture is not by the results of a single clinical trial, but through a detailed summary of all trials published to date, regardless of their results – an exercise scientists call 'systematic review'.

About 20 systematic reviews have been published. Based on such evidence, we are now reasonably sure that acupuncture is effective for back pain, dental pain, migraine and nausea.

Other systematic reviews have shown inconclusive overall results. Either the findings of reliable studies were contradictory or the majority of the trials were too flawed to be reliable. Ailments for which this is the case include addictions (other than nicotine), asthma, headache, inflammatory rheumatic conditions, neck pain, osteoarthritis and stroke. Finally, two systematic reviews show that for giving up smoking or weight loss, acupuncture is no more effective than a dummy treatment.

> ### The best evidence available to date is positive, but it also shows that acupuncture is not a 'cure-all'

It is interesting to compare this evidence with the results of surveys assessing the complaints acupuncturists actually treat.

Traditional acupuncturists in this country see mainly patients with musculoskeletal problems, emotional and psychological problems, arthritis, 'low energy' and digestive problems. Western acupuncturists treat musculoskeletal problems, pain in general, neurological conditions, allergies and addictions, as well as ear, nose and throat conditions.

And what about safety? The public often believes that complementary therapies are inherently risk-free and acupuncture is no exception. Yet there are numerous accounts of minor adverse effects associated with the treatment.

Discomfort or pain during the procedure or slight dizziness and tiredness afterwards are probably the most common complaints. Much more serious complications are also occasionally reported: trauma through needling and infections where non-sterile needles have been used.

These events are most likely to be genuine rarities, but more research needs to be done to be absolutely sure. With proper training of all acupuncturists, the incidence of serious adverse effects could probably be reduced even further.

So, what is the bottom line? Does acupuncture do more good than harm?

The best evidence available to date is positive, but it also shows that acupuncture is not a 'cure-all'. More research is needed to define when it might be dangerous, when it is harmless – but also not helpful – and when it offers more benefits than conventional medicine.

• Professor Ernst is Director of Complementary Medicine at the University of Exeter.

© Telegraph Group Limited,
London 2000

Gentle remedies

Despite the huge popularity of homeopathy, many doctors remain highly sceptical about it. But now a scientific study shows that this 200-year-old practice can help patients with allergies. Luisa Dillner on the pills that 'cure like with like'.

It's a form of medicine that has been around for nearly 200 years, with advocates as diverse as John D. Rockefeller, Mahatma Gandhi, Tina Turner and the royal family. But even though homeopathy is used by more than 20% of people and is available on the NHS, no one knows how it works. And yet it does seem to work. A research paper in last week's *British Medical Journal* shows that out of 50 people with nasal allergies, 28% improved with homeopathy compared with 3% given a placebo. While symptoms of blocked, runny or itchy nose, eye irritation and sneezing got better over four weeks in both groups, those on homeopathic treatment had better nasal air flow and could therefore breathe more easily.

Dr David Reilly of the Glasgow Homeopathy Hospital, one of the paper's authors, hopes his results will encourage doctors to look again at the evidence supporting homeopathy. 'Despite these findings, and the fact that there have now been more than 180 trials of homeopathy – of which 70% are positive – there will still be doctors who believe religiously that it cannot work and therefore it does not work,' he says.

Homeopathy was invented by Samuel Hahnemann, a German doctor who was so horrified by the cures available in the late 18th century, such as blood letting and arsenic, that he gave up his traditional practice. Using drugs such as belladonna, he experimented on himself and announced a new medical principle (based on the practice of the ancient Greeks) of 'that which makes sick shall heal'.

Homeopathy, from a combination of the Greek words for similar and suffering, works on the basis that like cures like. Cutting onions, for example, makes your nose and eyes run and your throat sore. So what better treatment for a cold, in

By Luisa Dillner

homeopathic terms, than *Allium cepa*, a remedy made from onion? Homeopaths cite parallels in conventional medicine to support this concept – irradiation causes cancer but also treats it, and digitalis can both cause and cure irregular heart rates. But while conventional medicine gives doses you can measure, homeopathy does not. Homeopathy believes that only a tiny amount of like cures like and uses medicines that contain minute doses of the therapeutic agent. The medicines, from plants, minerals, metals and even poisons, are serially diluted in alcohol and water, up to many thousands of times. Each time they are diluted they are vigorously shaken and each dilution is thought to make the remedy stronger.

Remedies come in various forms, often as tablets. The problem that critics have is that after the 12th centesimal dilution, no molecules of the original substance can be found in these remedies. A biochemical analysis shows only water and alcohol. How, they ask, can homeopathy work when its remedies contain no active agents?

'Many people say there is no plausible mechanism for it to work and that trials are a waste of money,' says Dr Reilly. 'Now if people tell you there's a unicorn at the end of your garden you can invoke plausibility and refuse to believe it. But if over 200 years people keep saying there's a unicorn in your garden then it might be at least worth having a look.'

Reilly and others believe that homeopathic remedies are active because the water and alcohol remember, in some way, the original ingredient. 'There may be some imprinting of information from the starting material in the first dilution,' he says.

Regardless of how effective the remedies are, homeopathy's growing popularity is partly due to the consultation process. Practitioners may take over an hour seeing patients and specifically ask about emotions and life stresses. Dr Reilly says: 'If a patient comes in with asthma then we ask what was going on in their life when it started. They may tell you

HAYFEVER? ...WHAT HAYFEVER?

that they had some devastating grief and their health went right down and they got asthma. Part of the prescribing may be a remedy for what we call illness from grief. Extracting the history from a patient is quite therapeutic for them – it shows we are interested not just in the diagnosis but how the disease affects them.' So therapeutic is the consultation that for years it, rather than the remedies, was credited with making patients better. But a study of more than 100 homeopathy trials, published in the *Lancet* in 1997, found that the consultation alone could not explain homeopathy's clinical effects.

Remedies are tailored to individuals to take account of the person's experience of their disease – what time of the day or during which weather conditions their symptoms are worst. Rather than attacking the agent responsible, they are said to provoke the body's own defence mechanisms. Symptoms are matched with remedies from the homeopathic materia medica and patients may also be told to make lifestyle and dietary changes. Patients are usually reviewed between two and six weeks when their practitioner may stop treatment and monitor progress.

Homeopathy's underlying tenet, which rankles with many doctors, is that there are no incurable diseases for homeopathy, only incurable patients. But homeopathy does not claim to clear any mechanical obstructions or fractures. These, they admit, need surgical treatment. Most registered homeopaths would not treat patients with cancer without conventional help. There are more than 1,000 doctors and at least 1,500 non-doctors in the UK practising homeopathy.

Francis Truherz trained as a homeopath and has practised for 10 years, mostly in NHS clinics in London. 'Sometimes patients come to see me without seeing their GP and I will strongly advise them to see a doctor. I may not always get it right, but then doctors can also miss diagnoses,' he says. 'If someone phoned me and said they thought they had meningitis I'd tell them to phone for an ambulance.'

As with conventional medicines, homeopathy is increasingly

Arnica (mountain daisy): for minor bumps and bruises.

Aconite: for shock, intense fear, violent emotions, restlessness with fear of death.

Chamomilla (chamomille): for teething infants.

Coffea (coffee): for insomnia.

Colocynthis: for infant colic.

Rhus tox (poison ivy): for joint pains worse with first movement and rest and then better with motion, for joint stiffness in damp weather, for back pain and stiffness.

Cuprum: for leg cramps.

Comfrey: relieves pain from fractures after they have been treated surgically.

Calendula: for cuts and grazes, helps heal wounds. Use as ointment, gel or spray.

Urtica urens (stinging nettles): for burns.

available over the counter. 'It's fine to try them – you can't overdose on them as you can with aspirin,' says Truherz. 'If your symptoms persist, see your doctor or registered homeopath. It's really matching the prescription to the patient that makes the remedy homeopathic.' He advises people to use products from one of six licensed manufacturers (such as Helios or Ainsworths). Homeopathic medicines must be taken in a clean mouth (no eating for 20 minutes before and no toothpaste or cigarettes) and he advises no coffee for a month once treatment starts because it can neutralise remedies.

Andrew Vickers, researcher and author of the *ABC of Complementary Medicine* (BMJ Publishing Group), says that it's still as easy to argue against homeopathy as to argue for it. For a start, he says, there's enormous variation in remedies and practice, with some homeopaths using low dilutions and others high. Some only give one remedy at a time, others give combinations. In France they may prepare a remedy by macerating it in alcohol for two days, in Germany by leaving it in alcohol

for 12 days. 'We did a study where we gave two homeopaths a list of symptoms and said is it plausible to give this medicine? There was only mediocre agreement,' says Vickers. 'If you did an equivalent study asking doctors if it was plausible to give aspirin for headaches, they would almost all say yes.'

Vickers is also concerned that so much of homeopathy's knowledge base is unvalidated. 'Homeopathic repertories tell practitioners how to prescribe on the basis of patients' symptoms. But some symptoms are utterly bizarre, such as "erections during supper" and "dreams of writing on a dirty table and the paper becoming smeared".

'This information is un-referenced, it's just there. It comes from "provings" that involve healthy people being given potential homeopathic remedies and then recording and reporting everything that happens to them. The remedy and the recorded "symptoms" are then entered into the repertory. We analysed some provings that were done and people recorded "thoughts of hedgehogs" and "felt bored during lectures". There is no evidence that these potential remedies caused these symptoms.'

Vickers estimates that there are around 2,000 homeopathic remedies but believes that most homeopaths use a core of 30 or 40 that they are confident work for groups of symptoms. Even so there are no studies that show how these drugs can work. 'It's all highly implausible,' he says. 'A new cancer drug would be similar to an old cancer drug and there would be some work in animal models so you could believe it could work, and a clinical trial using patients would be part of a larger picture of evidence. With homeopathy there are no animal models. With homeopathy you need more evidence than normal to show it works because the clinical trials are all you have. But so far the data is largely positive from those clinical trials. Sceptics who try to argue against these trials can't make the positive findings go away. These are good trials.'

Peers say NHS could embrace alternative therapies

*By Sarah Boseley,
Health Editor*

A step was taken yesterday towards integration of complementary and alternative medicine into the NHS with a House of Lords select committee report that urged greater regulation but called for doctors and nurses to listen to patients' growing demands and recognise the potential for good of unconventional therapies.

After 15 months study the Lords select committee on science and technology produced a 140-page report that points a clear way forward through what has been a minefield for politicians in the past. It wants the NHS to make it easier for patients to gain access to therapies that work and give patients more and better information about what works and what does not.

The Lords does not embrace all the therapies, some with a spiritual dimension, which have taken off in the UK, but the report is careful not to tar any of them. Peers distinguish between those disciplines such as osteopathy and chiropractic that are well regulated and have good evidence to show they work, a second group of 'feel-good' therapies which complement conventional medicine and do no harm, and a third group which 'cannot be supported unless and until convincing research evidence of efficacy, based upon the results of well-designed trials, can be produced'.

The one point of serious controversy in the report is likely to be the inclusion of traditional Chinese medicine and Ayurvedic medicine (an ancient Indian discipline) in the third list of unproven treatments. Both disciplines go back thousands of years and are extensively practised in China and India.

Asked if he would use any of the complementary and alternative medicine remedies, Lord Walton of Detchant, who chaired the sub-committee running the inquiry, said: 'I would have no difficulty at all if I had troublesome back pain which was not helped by visits to the doctor in consulting an osteopath or a chiropractor. If I was in intolerable pain, I'd at least consider acupuncture. I'd be perfectly prepared to consider herbal remedies that are shown by research to be effective forms of treatment.'

The one point of serious controversy in the report is likely to be the inclusion of traditional Chinese medicine and Ayurvedic medicine

He would also consider aromatherapy and other complementary therapies listed in the report's second group. But he said: 'I would not personally be willing to take advantage of any in group three.'

The Lords acknowledged the rise of alternative medicine was driven by public demand, fuelled by distrust of conventional drugs and disillusion with doctors who could spare them only a few minutes. A therapist, by contrast, would spend up to an hour discussing the emotional as well as physical problems of the patient.

The committee felt there was a need for the public to be given better information and to be helped to find reputable, trained and accredited practitioners. Members recognised a danger that some people would turn their back on conventional drugs to embrace alternative 'cures' that made them feel better but failed to tackle the underlying disease which might be killing them.

Much more research into alternative therapies was needed, the report said, recommending that the NHS and the Medical Research Council should put in money to develop centres of excellence akin to the successful National Center for Complementary Alternative Medicine in the United States. Randomised controlled trials, which were required of any conventional medicine, should be carried out to establish how well alternative therapies work.

There have been some such trials of herbal remedies, which have established that St. John's Wort or hypericum, for instance, is effective against depression. But most herbal medicines have not been tested in this way and problems can arise when mixtures are used. The committee said there was good evidence of the efficacy of osteopathy and chiropractic, which could be more effective than physiotherapy, and of acupuncture for pain relief and treatment of nausea.

Committee members were 'sceptical about the modes of action of most of the others', said the report, but they accepted many of the group two therapies helped relieve stress.

There was no reason why homoeopathy, which was already provided on the NHS, should work – patients were given minuscule doses of whatever was deemed to be causing their problem – but they accepted that it might have a beneficial effect because patients believed it was helping them.

Tighter regulation of alternative medicine practitioners was vital, said the report, and only those disciplines which were well regulated should be accessible through the NHS. Acupuncture and herbal medicine should be subject to statutory regulation and there should be a clampdown on misleading labels on herbal medicines, which sometimes made unjustified claims.

The report found favour on all sides. The Royal College of Nursing was in favour of more regulation and training and the commitment to patient choice and protection.

Peter Fisher, clinical director of the NHS Royal London Homoeopathic hospital, said: 'We're quite happy with it. We can't really argue with their main points about high quality information, regulation, which has been a very high priority for us, and research and NHS provision.'

© *Guardian Newspapers Limited 2000*

Chinese herbal medicine

Safety matters

Answers to common questions compiled for your assistance by the Register of Chinese Herbal Medicine (RCHM).

Are herbs safe?

Chinese herbs are very safe when prescribed correctly by a properly trained practitioner, and adverse reactions are extremely rare. Chinese Herbal Medicine has a continuous tradition dating back more than two thousand years, and throughout its long history practitioners have placed great emphasis on safe and effective treatment. Over the centuries, generations of doctors and scholars have compiled detailed information about the herbs, which forms an unprecedented body of knowledge available to the modern practitioner, enabling high standards of practice and safety. Detailed knowledge of this information is required of all RCHM Members.

In order to ensure that your case is properly diagnosed and monitored, it is recommended that you consult a registered practitioner of Chinese Herbal Medicine who will take a full case history including details of your previous medical history and prescribed medication you may be taking.

You should be able to communicate easily with your practitioner and be able to discuss any concerns you may have about your treatment. Your practitioner will provide you with written instructions on how and when to take the herbs, and a contact number you can phone in the event of any questions. Whilst taking Chinese herbs your practitioner will see you regularly to monitor your progress. If you are given a pre-packaged herbal product it should be clearly labelled in English listing all the ingredients and have an expiry date and a batch number. Do not take any product which does not have this clear labelling.

I have heard that herbs can cause liver damage. Is this true?

In very rare cases a patient may develop an allergic type of reaction to an ingredient in a Chinese herbal formula, leading to Liver injury. If treatment is stopped as soon as such symptoms occur, no lasting damage will occur. This type of reaction may occur with any medicine, including pharm-aceutical drugs. The most common manifestation of this kind of reaction is a combination of non-specific symptoms, usually of sudden onset, such as: severe tiredness, loss of appetite, nausea, upper abdominal pain, feeling generally unwell, jaundice. None of these symptoms is, in itself, indicative of an allergic response to Chinese herbs, but nevertheless, if any of these symptoms occur, you should stop taking your herbs and contact your practitioner who will use his or her professional judgement to advise you accordingly. It is very important if you have had this kind of adverse reaction to Chinese herbs that you on no account start taking herbs again unless you are being properly supervised by a qualified practitioner.

This type of extremely rare reaction should not be confused with the minor transitory reactions that some people can experience when first taking herbs, such as slight nausea or loose stools, because of initially being unused to taking herbal medicines. Such symptoms should always be reported to your practitioner, who will be able to reassure you.

I have also heard that Chinese herbs can lead to kidney damage. Is this true?

The cases of kidney damage that have been reported concern the use of plant species that belong to the genus Aristolochia, which contain Aristolochic acids. The supply of any species of Aristolochia is now illegal in Britain, and will not be included in any herbal prescription dispensed by a registered practitioner.

How is the quality of the herbs controlled?

The need for herbal quality control has led to the recent formation of the Chinese Medicine Association of Suppliers (CMAS) who supply members of the RCHM with their herbs. CMAS has a Code of Good Practice and are currently working together with Kew Gardens as part of their commitment to provide authenticated high quality herbs. Systems are currently being implemented to ensure that the correct herbal species are being imported and supplied to the UK market. The best way to ensure you are getting the right herbs is to be certain that your herbal practitioner purchases their herbs from a member of CMAS.

Finding your nearest registered practitioner
The Register of Chinese Herbal Medicine can supply you with a list of qualified practitioners in your area. All RCHM Members have achieved recognised standards of qualification, have full professional insurance and are bound by Codes of Conduct and Good Practice. Please feel free to contact the office and we will be happy to assist you in any way we can. See page 41 for address details.

• The above information is an extract from the safety matters leaflet produced by the RHHM. Contact them for a full version.

Watchdog to police Chinese cures

By Robin McKie, Science Editor

They have become some of Britain's most successful treatments for chronic illness, generating an industry worth more than £100 million a year.

Chinese herbal medicines – first used 3,000 years ago – are now big business and used to treat everything from eczema to rheumatoid arthritis. Last year more than a million prescriptions were issued to British people. Treatments typically involve taking a few mouthfuls of concocted brews – a simple, harmless business, according to practitioners.

But this cosy image has recently been destroyed by doctors uncovering cases of near-fatal incidents in which patients were given incorrect drugs. In one case, two women suffered serious kidney damage when they took the herbal preparation Aristolochia instead of the harmless drug Stephania.

Similar confusion led to an outbreak – involving more than 70 people – of kidney failures in Belgium. As a result, Aristolochia is now banned in Britain and many other countries.

In another study, researchers in London uncovered more than a dozen cases of liver disease triggered by traditional Chinese prescriptions for eczema.

Many experts fear that increasing numbers of people could be given incorrect, sometimes dangerous, doses as the use of Chinese herbal medicines soars, and as numbers of practitioners – of whom there are now more than 4,000 in the UK – continue to rise. The problem, they stress, is not one of malpractice, but of an inability to identify herbs accurately.

This alarming scenario has had unexpected consequences: the establishment of a unique scientific collaboration between Oriental doctors and Western scientists. Together they have set up an authentication centre at Kew Gardens for pinpointing Chinese medicinal herbs.

The scheme – backed by medical herb importers and by the Chinese government – is aimed at preventing future poisoning outbreaks. 'There are more than 500 herbs, used by traditional Chinese doctors, and these are being imported in increasing amounts to Britain,' said Dr Christine Leon, head of Kew's Chinese Medicinal Plants Authentication Centre.

More than 10,000 tonnes of Chinese herbs were imported into Britain last year, although estimates suggest a quarter of this traffic is still incorrectly labelled.

For example, one drug, picked at random from Leon's collection, was labelled heartwood of Aquilaria. Chinese doctors claim its resin has powerful, anti-indigestion properties.

'Unfortunately, the sample I have here indicates it has been coated with black paint at some time, and that is unlikely to be conducive to good digestion,' she added. Since setting up the authentication service, with the support of Britain's major importers of Chinese herbal medicines, Leon has made a series of visits to China, returning with bundles of herbs, details of their habitats, and their dried stems, pieces of which are boiled and given to patients. These samples will form the basis of her centre's herbal medicine collection.

Importers or doctors unsure about the identity of a particular herb will then be able to bring it to the Kew centre to have it identified. 'We are even planning to take DNA samples so we can be really sure we know what we are dealing with, although we still need several years, and another £500,000 to complete the project,' added Leon.

This should lead to a merging of two very different intellectual disciplines, Martin Powell, a herbal medicine practitioner and consultant for the import company, East-West Natural Health Ltd, pointed out.

Powell said that, although the West was conquering acute, life-threatening illnesses such as heart disease or kidney failure, it had had far less success with chronic, long-term illnesses – such as skin complaints, rheumatoid arthritis and irritable bowel syndrome. These ailments are considered most likely to respond to the herbal medications of ancient China.

'Chinese medicine started to become popular with the spreading success of acupuncture,' he added. 'It is an ancient art but it still has something to offer, I believe.'

• First published in *The Observer*, April 2000.

ADDITIONAL RESOURCES

You might like to contact the following organisations for further information. Due to the increasing cost of postage, many organisations cannot respond to enquiries unless they receive a stamped, addressed envelope.

British Medical Acupuncture Society (BMAS)
12 Marbury House
Higher Whitley
Warrington, WA4 4QW
Tel: 01925 730727
Fax: 01925 730492
E-mail: Admin@medical-acupuncture.org.uk
Web site: www.medical-acupuncture.co.uk
The BMAS promotes the use of acupuncture as therapy following orthodox medical diagnosis by suitably trained practitioners.

The British Reflexology Association
Monk's Orchard
Whitbourne
Worcester, WR6 5RB
Tel: 01886 821207
Fax: 01886 822017
E-mail: bra@britreflex.co.uk
Web site: www.britreflex.co.uk
The British Reflexology Association was founded in 1985 to act as a representative body for persons practising the method of reflexology as a profession and for students training in the method.

Christian Medical Fellowship (CMF)
157 Waterloo Road
London, SE1 8XN
Tel: 020 7928 4694
Fax: 020 7620 2453
E-mail: info@cmf.org.uk
Web site: www.cmf.org.uk
A network of over 4,500 doctors in all branches of medicine, and over 1,000 medical students, throughout the UK and Republic of Ireland. It publishes a range of booklets and leaflets.

The Dr Edward Bach Centre
Mount Vernon
Bakers Lane
Sotwell
Oxon, OX10 0PZ
Tel: 01491 834678
Fax: 01491 825022
Web site: www.bachcentre.com
This was the home and workplace of Dr Bach in the last years of his life, when he completed his research into the flower remedies that still bear his name.

General Osteopathic Council
Osteopathy House
176 Tower Bridge Street
London, SE1 3LU
Tel: 020 7357 6655
Fax: 020 7357 0011
E-mail: info@osteopathy.org.uk
Web site: www.osteopathy.org.uk
The General Osteopathic Council offers an information service where you can obtain factsheets, have your questions answered and find addresses of registered osteopaths.

Institute for Complementary Medicine (ICM)
PO Box 194
London, SE16 1QZ
Tel: 020 7237 5165
Fax: 020 7237 5175
E-mail: icm@icmedicine.co.uk
Web site: www.icmedicine.co.uk
The ICM is a focal point of learning and healing for those concerned with the future of health.

National Institute of Medical Herbalists (NIMH)
56 Longbrook Street
Exeter, EX4 6AH
Tel: 01392 426022
Fax: 01392 498963
Web site: www.btinternet.com/~nimh/
The NIMH is the UK's leading professional organisation of practitioners of herbal medicine.

The Natural Medicines Society (NMS)
PO Box 232
East Molesey, KT8 1YF
Tel: 020 8974 1166
Fax: 020 8974 1166
E-mail: nms@charity.vfree.com
Web site: www.thenms.demon.co.uk
The only UK consumer body that defends your freedom to use alternative and complementary medicines and therapies.

The Register of Chinese Herbal Medicine (RCHM)
PO Box 400
Wembley, HA9 9NZ
Tel: 07000 790332
Fax: 07000 790332
E-mail: herbmed@rchm.co.uk
Web site: www.rchm.co.uk
The RCHM was set up in 1987 to regulate the practice of Chinese Herbal Medicine (CHM) in the UK.

The Register of Qualified Aromatherapists (RQA)
PO Box 3431
Danbury
Chelmsford, CM3 4UA
Tel: 01245 227957
Fax: 01245 222152
E-mail: admin@rqa-uk.org
Web site: www.rqa-uk.org
The RQA is a professional association of aromatherapy practitioners who have undergone training of the highest standards.

The Reiki Association
Cornbrook Bridge House
Cornbrook, Clee Hill
Ludlow, SY8 3QQ
Tel: 01584 891197
Fax: 01584 890284
E-mail: reikiassoc_office@compuserve.com
Web site: www.reikiassociation.org.uk
The Reiki Association is an association of people initiated into Reiki. Help line open 3pm-6pm Monday to Friday. Tel. 01981 550829.

The Society of Homeopaths
4a Artizan Road
Northampton, NN1 4HU
Tel: 01604 621400
Fax: 01604 622622
E-mail: societyofhomeopaths@btinternet.com
The Society of Homeopaths is the professional body for homeopaths practising in the Hahnemannian tradition.

INDEX

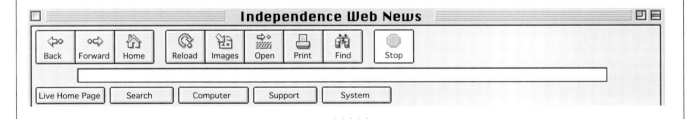

★ ★ ★ ★ ★

The Internet has been likened to shopping in a supermarket without aisles. The press of a button on a Web browser can bring up thousands of sites but working your way through them to find what you want can involve long and frustrating on-line searches.

And unfortunately many sites contain inaccurate, misleading or heavily biased information. Our researchers have therefore undertaken an extensive analysis to bring you a selection of quality Web site addresses.

National Institute of Medical Herbalists

www.btinternet.com/~nimh/
From the home page you can access information about Herbs, Research, Education or Politics. You can also find your nearest practitioner in their online register of fully-qualified therapists.

General Osteopaths Council

www.osteopathy.org.uk
On the Osteopathic Information Service web site you can find fact sheets including Looking after yourself in your Teens and Twenties.

British Homeopathic Association (BHA)

www.trusthomeopathy.org/faculty
From this home page you have three options: Faculty of Homeopathy, British Homeopathic Association or The Case for Homeopathy. From each of these choices you can find out information on homeopathy, treatments and education and training respectively.

New York Online Access to Health (NOAH)

www.noah-health.org
At the home page, click on Health Topics which takes you to a long list including Alternative Medicine. Within this link there are hundreds or articles on Complementary Medicine. Well worth a visit.

British Acupuncture Council

www.acupuncture.org.uk
This site is where you will find helpful and representative information about all aspects of acupuncture and particularly traditional acupuncture as practised in the United Kingdom.

The Dr Edward Bach Centre

www.bachcentre.com
From this home page you can visit either The Dr Edward Bach Centre, The Dr Edward Bach Foundation or The Dr Edward Bach Healing Trust. At the centre you can find out all about Bach Flower Remedies.

ACKNOWLEDGEMENTS

The publisher is grateful for permission to reproduce the following material.

While every care has been taken to trace and acknowledge copyright, the publisher tenders its apology for any accidental infringement or where copyright has proved untraceable. The publisher would be pleased to come to a suitable arrangement in any such case with the rightful owner.

Chapter One: Overview

What is complementary medicine?, © 2000 ICM (Institute for Complementary Medicine), *Herbal cocktails to lead revolution in medicines*, © The Independent Newspaper Ltd, 2000, *Complementary therapies*, © Arthritis Research Campaign (ARC), *Homeopathy*, © The Society of Homoepaths, *Reflexology*, © Linda Dooley, *What is reflexology?*, © The British Reflexology Association, *What is aromatherapy?*, © The Register of Qualified Aromatherapists (RQA), *Acupuncture: an overview*, © British Medical Acupuncture Society (BMAS), *Osteopathy*, © General Osteopathic Council, *Iridology*, © Holistic Health Consultancy London, *The Natural Medicines Society*, © The Natural Medicines Society (NMS), *The Register of Chinese Herbal Medicine*, © The Register of Chinese Herbal Medicine (RCHM), *Herbal medicine*, © The National Institute of Medicine Herbalists, *What is healing?*, © 2000 ICM (Institute for Complementary Medicine), *Healing and medicine*, © Doctor-Healer Network, *Reiki*, © The Reiki Association, *Healing the emotions*, © The Dr Edward Bach Centre.

Chapter Two: The Debate

Questioning the alternative, © The Wellcome Trust, *A little drop of flower power*, © Telegraph Group Limited, London 2000, *Alternative medicine*, © Christian Medical Fellowship (CMF), *What is complementary medicine?*, © British Medical Journal, 1999; 319:693-696. (With permission from the BMJ Publishing Group), *It works – up to a point*, © Telegraph Group Limited, London 2000, *Gentle remedies*, © Guardian Newspapers Limited, 2000, *Peers say NHS could embrace alternative therapies*, © Guardian Newspapers Limited 2000, *Chinese herbal medicine*, © The Register of Chinese Herbal Medicine (RCHM), *Watchdog to police Chinese cures*, © Jim Pollard.

Photographs and illustrations:

Pages 1, 2, 5, 8, 9, 12, 14, 18, 21, 22, 26, 31, 36: Pumpkin House, 6, 10, 15, 19, 24, 27, 28, 35, 40: Simon Kneebone.

Craig Donnellan
Cambridge
January, 2001